RODNEY EDWARDS is an award-winning journalist with *The Impartial Reporter* in Enniskillen, County Fermanagh, and appears regularly on local radio and television stations. He also contributes to newspapers and magazines in Belfast, London and Dublin. He was named Northern Ireland Weekly Journalist of the Year in 2013, and in 2014 was voted tenth most influential UK journalist on Twitter by *Press Gazette*. This is his first book.

Sure, Why Would Ye Not?

RODNEY EDWARDS

·THE·
BLACK
·STAFF·
PRESS

First published in 2015 by
Blackstaff Press
4D Weavers Court
Linfield Road
Belfast
BT12 5GH

with the assistance of
The Arts Council of Northern Ireland

Designed by seagulls.net
Typeset by KT Designs, St Helens, England
Printed in Berwick-upon-Tweed by Martins the Printers

ISBN 978-0-85640-963-9

www.blackstaffpress.com
www.rodneyedwards.co.uk

Follow Rodney Edwards on Twitter @rodneyedwards

To Mum and Dad,

and my goddaughter Sophie Thornton,

with love

Contents

A wee note about two oul fellas, Bob and Charlie   ix

1   On the Farm   1

2   Family   16

3   Runnin' the Roads   33

4   From the Cradle to the Grave   42

5   Days Out   57

6   Clannin' about the House   74

7   Health and Wealth   96

8   Themuns   119

9   Atein' an' Drinkin'   133

10   The Weather   147

11   Not in My Day   164

A wee note about two oul fellas, Bob and Charlie

All over Ireland, north and south, are old men hashin'. They are standing in fields, they are leaning against gates, they are sitting on walls, they are drinking cups of tay and putting the world to rights. You see them everywhere – on farms, in shops, at funerals, at the ends of roads – never more than two at a time and usually wearing wellies and flat caps. They complain, they laugh, they reminisce, they help one another and they speak in the unique language of the rural communities in which they live.

It was meeting so many of these wonderful characters that inspired me to start a column in *The Impartial Reporter*, looking at the local lingo. 'Fermanagh Spake' – featuring short conversations between farmers Bob and Charlie – celebrates the uniqueness of Irish turns of phrase and shines a light on a much-loved part of country life and culture.

Two years on, the column is still enormously popular with readers of all ages and, thanks to the internet, Bob and Charlie's antics are known and loved throughout Ireland and further afield, proving to me that this kind of hashin' is not unique to Fermanagh. After much thought, and following requests from readers, the obvious next step for the two oul fellas was a book.

Bob or Charlie may remind you of your father, grandfather, uncle or neighbour. Their conversations may remind you of home, of growing up, of family life. You may even feel a little nostalgic. It is my genuine hope that Bob and Charlie and their friends don't just make you laugh but that they also remind you of how special the Irish spirit is.

Put the kettle on, butter some Veda, and sit back and have a bit of craic. Sure, why would ye not?

Chapter One
On the Farm

To clan about, *to mess around*

Bob: Yer man's cub is givin' me a hand to draw the bales.

Charlie: Who would that be now? Tom's cub? Thon boy would be no age – can he handle the work at all?

Bob: Oh aye, though he has one leg shorter than the other.

Charlie: Is that right?

Bob: He does an awful bit of limpin' about.

Charlie: An' would he be a hardy worker?

Bob: He'd be dead on if he'd stop clannin' about.

To footer

Bob: Howya the day?

Charlie: Flat out – I've the sheep to dip. Yerself?

Bob: I've the bottom field to cut before she pours out of the heavens.

Charlie: It gives rain surely – ye may be quick.

Bob: I'll stick the jacket on, then so.

Charlie: Did ye get that fence painted last night?

Bob: I did a wee bit of footerin' after me tea, so I did, but then the midges ate the arms off me an' I had to leave it.

Yoke, *an object or thing*

~~~~~~

Bob: Japers, would ye look at her! Can she do many miles to the gallon?

Charlie: Oh she can surely. There's some roar off her.

Bob: She's shinin', boys. Ye must have claned her.

Charlie: The cub ran the hose over her this mornin' for she was boggin'.

Bob: There's a hitch on there, is there?

Charlie: Oh aye, ye'd get a cattle trailer on her no bother.

Bob: I tell ye what, she's some yoke.

To faff about

~~~~~~

Bob: Have ye got the Single Farm Payment yet?

Charlie: I have not. I phoned up about it, but could I get through on that buckin' number? Such a bit of faffin' about.

Bob: Ye need to go on that 'puter till ye see. That's what Thornton did.

Charlie: I wouldn' even know how to turn thon thing on.

Bob: See did they send ye one of them email things.

Charlie: The snow will be on the ground before I see that.

Brute of a thing

Bob: The cow dropped dead last night.

Charlie: Och, it did not. The Limousin?

Bob: That's the one. There was an almighty clatter in the middle of *Coronation Street*. I threw the wellies on an' came up here an' there she was flat on her back, boy.

Charlie: Did ye get her moved all right?

Bob: The wife give me a hand. She was an awful brute of a thing.

Boggin', *dirty*

Bob: I've been diggin' up thon yard of mine all day. The sweat's rollin' off me.

Charlie: What has ye at that?

Bob: I need to lay a pipe from the hen house to the piggery.

Charlie: I thought ye did that no time ago.

Bob: Sure she's leakin' away the whole time.

Charlie: Is it bad?

Bob: There was a burst pipe durin' the frost.

Charlie: Will it be a boyo to fix?

Bob: Well, I need it done or there'll be no watter in the trough.

Charlie: Ye'd want to get it done, then so.

Bob: I know. It's a fierce dorty oul job though. I'm boggin'.

Quarely stuck

Charlie: Japers, would ye look at Thornton's van. What happened her?

Bob: He was deliverin' a lock of eggs this mornin' an' lost control of her comin' down the hill.

Charlie: An' bang into yer greenhouse.

Bob: Straight through the whole thing. It was lucky nobody was kilt.

Charlie: Will ye get her lifted out of that?

Bob: The brother's comin' now with a rope for she's quarely stuck.

Trampin' the fields

Bob: I'm never done, that's the truth.

Charlie: Did ye get thon field finished?

Bob: I've been sowin' fertiliser all mornin'.

Charlie: How long will it take ye? Bailey's lookin' for us to help with the milkin'.

Bob: I'll be trampin' the fields another while, that's for sure.

I've a cow calvin'

Bob: Me an' the fellas are away to the mart. Are ye comin'?

Charlie: I don't think I'll get to it at all. I've a cow calvin'.

Bob: We'll not be long, sure - ye'll be back in an hour or so in time for yer dinner.

Charlie: I can't do one thing. Thon heifer's teats are fillin' up.

Bob: Ye may stay with her then.

Charlie: Is right, I can't go anywhere.

Keep 'er lit, *keep going; don't stop*
Street, *yard*

Bob: Me back is broke cuttin' sticks, that's the truth.

Charlie: Have ye many to do?

Bob: I've thirteen bags to fill for Father Curry.

Charlie: Does he need all of them?

Bob: He says it gives snow the mara. I've another three to do an' then I'm stoppin' for a drop of tay.

Charlie: Here, ye may keep 'er lit: Curry's not a man for waitin'. He'll be on that street in no time.

Are ye about the mara?

Bob: Them hens have quit layin', ye know. That's the second time this week.

Charlie: What would be wrong with them?

Bob: I haven't a notion, but I need to have a gander.

Charlie: They need to be layin' before the county show.

Bob: Don't I know it. The wife's expectin' them eggs to win the whole thing again.

Charlie: I've to go to Mr Bell's wake, but I can give ye a hand first.

Bob: Sure, ye go on. Are ye about the mara?

Sheugh, *an open ditch or drain*

Bob: That boy next dur is goin' stone mad.

Charlie: Is he moanin' about the muck on the road again?

Bob: Not this time. No, he's lost the head because his bull calf got out on him last night.

Charlie: Japers - no wonder he's ragin'. Has he found it?

Bob: He has, but it's got stuck.

Charlie: That's all thon boy needs. Where?

Bob: It's stuck in the sheugh.

A rake of work, *a considerable amount of work*

Bob: Bailey's had me milkin' since the crack of dawn.

Charlie: Ye're hard at it. I suppose ye have nearly all done.

Bob: Father Curry's lookin' more sticks. He says his bones are cowl.

Charlie: Do ye ever rest at all?

Bob: I'll rest plenty when I'm dead.

Charlie: Ye're right there, so ye are.

Bob: There's nohin' like gettin' a rake of work done.

Grazin'

Charlie: We need to get the hole in thon fence fixed.

Bob: I've the toolbox in the boot of the car.

Charlie: There's a right bit of damage.

Bob: That's young drivers for ye.

Charlie: There would have been a bit of ice on the road.

Bob: There was probably a bit of speedin' goin' on too.

Charlie: Whatever happened, I need that fence fixed before the sheep are out grazin'.

Clart, *a person who makes a mess*

Bob: Was yer cub any good diggin' the spuds for ye?

Charlie: He wasn't the best, if I'm bein' honest.

Bob: What did he do wrong?

Charlie: He couldn' dig the thing half right - he made an awful mess in that back field.

Bob: I can't get over that, an' him diggin' spuds since he was no height.

Charlie: Nor can the wife. Then he tramped muck all over the house, the clart.

Do ye mind? *Do you remember?*

Bob: Are ye comin' to the bingo the night?

Charlie: I don't think I'll have time to tell ye the truth.

Bob: What are ye at?

Charlie: The wife has me doin' that Zumba.

Bob: What would that be about?

Charlie: Dancin' about the place like an eejit.

Bob: Ye'd rather go to the bingo then?

Charlie: Ye're right I would.

Bob: There's a big prize of £150 an' a rooster.

Charlie: Jaysus, that'd be all right.

Bob: That fox ate me last rooster, do ye mind?

Charlie: I mind it well. Feathers everywhere.

Bob: So ye'll come for a bit anyway?

Charlie: Och no, I can't. I've the fodder to do.

Get-away-ah-that, *you must be joking*

Bob: Ye aren't lookin' for a few round bales, are ye?

Charlie: I wouldn' mind a few, all right. I'll need 'em soon enough.

Bob: It's the good stuff I have.

Charlie: Is it indeed. How much ye lookin'?

Bob: Give me thirty pouns a bale.

Charlie: Get-away-ah-that – Thornton's sellin' them for fifteen.

Bob: I'll take twenty-five an' no less.

Charlie: Ye're not serious.

Bob: I am, an' I'll draw them in a link box an' all.

Charlie: Och, would ye quit.

Grape, *a pitchfork*

Bob: Have you a long-handled grape handy? Didn' I lend mine to the cub, an' he's away in a campervan to Donegal for the weekend.

Charlie: I do surely – it's lyin' on that street there, beside the pointy shovel.

Bob: Here, thon is a quare job for grapin' silage. Ye don't have to stoop as much. I'd have a wile bad back anyway, but only for me own grape I don't know what I'd do, that's the truth.

Charlie: The wife uses it all the time when she's clannin' about out here.

Bob: It gets the work done.

Charlie: Och, ye'd fairly need it when ye're worked to the bone.

No second cut the year, *when poor weather conditions prevent a second cut of silage*

Bob: Lookin' at the weather an' it doesn' look great.

Charlie: The ground is swimmin', so it is.

Bob: It gives it like that for the next fortnight.

Charlie: There's no point bringin' a tractor out in thon.

Bob: Sure ye'd only get it bogged to the belly.

Charlie: There'll be no second cut the year.

Ye'll not find till winter, *a colloquial acknowledgement that the coldest season of the year is on its way*

Bob: Sure that's like a winter's day.

Charlie: We'll not get much work done at all now.

Bob: I had to throw on two pairs of long johns this mornin'.

Charlie: I have a wee flask of tay with me that the wife made me.

Bob: Japers, aren't you lucky. My wife would give me a clip 'round the ear quicker.

Charlie: It's that cowl the animals are standin' with a hump on them behind that ditch.

Bob: Ye'll not find till winter.

To dose the calves, *to administer a vaccine to cattle to prevent, for example, fluke and worms*

Bob: It's nearly five o'clock, look, an' we're still not done.

Charlie: Here, 'mon till we dose these calves now.

Bob: I'll lift this one by the back of the leg.

Charlie: Watch he doesn' give ye a clout.

Bob: I mind the time Thornton did this an' the calf dunged over his welly.

Charlie: Sure I've had the wellies covered in dung more times. The wife doesn' let me in the house now until I hose meself down.

Bob: Right, let's get these boyos done before it gets dark.

Charlie: We'll be ready for a drop of tay after we're finished.

To hit the diff, *to apply the differential lock on a tractor*

Bob: Japers Charlie, I doubt we are stuck.

Charlie: She's not movin' one iota at all.

Bob: Ye may call that cub of yers to give us a tow.

Charlie: We'll not need him, try her again there.

Bob: She's bogged into the ground surely.

Charlie [sings]: 'Oh hit the diff and pray, that she goes all the way. We're flat to the mat with the party hats and heading for the tay . . .'

No joy

Bob: Ah here, I am up to high doh the day.

Charlie: What have ye done now?

Bob: I was calfin' this mornin' an' didn' I lose the weddin' ring.

Charlie: Och ye did not. Where'd ye lose it?

Bob: Ye know exactly where I lost it.

Charlie: Get away! Up the ...? Ye're in for it now, boy.

Bob: That's right, she'll go absolutely mad.

Charlie: Are ye sure ye didn' just drop it somewhere on the yard?

Bob: I am sure for I've been lookin' all day.

Charlie: An' nohin'?

Bob: No joy at all. I better ring that vet - mind you, she's about as useful as an ashtray on a motorbike.

Don't be tellin' me that

Bob: Ah here, ye'll never guess what?

Charlie: What?

Bob: Mind the wiman came to collect the eggs?

Charlie: The sturdy wiman that owns all the pigeons?

Bob: Aye, she's about the width of thon shed dur.

Charlie: What about her?

Bob: She put the eggs in the front seat of that car of hers, then by the time she'd finished chattin', she forgot they were there an' sat bang on top of them.

Charlie: She did not.

Bob: She did, an' she made a clatty mess. Cryin' an' everyhin'.

Charlie: Don't be tellin' me that.

Put that in yer pipe an' smoke it, *to order someone to accept your point of view, even if they disagree with it*

Bob: Here, ye nearly ran over me foot in that tractor.

Charlie: Too bad I didn'. Better luck next time.

Bob: What's wrong, are ye huffin'?

Charlie: Ye sat on me good lunch box an' broke it.

Bob: I did not sit on yer lunch box.

Charlie: Ye must have, who else could have?

Bob: It was Thornton.

Charlie: Ye're only sayin' that to get out of a handlin'.

Bob: The arse of his overalls was covered in grated cheese.

Charlie: He'll be covered in blood when I get me hands on him.

Bob: So it wasn' me. Put that in yer pipe an' smoke it.

Chapter Two
Family

Ninety to the dozen, *at high speed (usually referring to speech)*

Bob: There's a message on this blinkin' phone from that lassie of mine.

Charlie: What's she after now?

Bob: I don't know – I can barely make her out.

Charlie: Let me have a listen.

Bob: There, do ye hear that? Somehin' about out shappin'.

Charlie: Is she sayin' she wants a hand to carry the groceries home?

Bob: She's talkin' too fast, that's the problem.

Charlie: I know, sure she's goin' ninety to the dozen.

He'll grow out of it

Bob: What age is yer eldest granchild now?

Charlie: He'd be twenty-somehin' at least.

Bob: An' what's he doin' with himself?

Charlie: Very little – he's away this weekend to see some band with that lassie of his.

Bob: That's the courtin' for ye, sends the head mad.

Charlie: Sure any time they're here they're never done smoochin'.

Bob: That'll not last long, all that clannin' about.

Charlie: Not at all, he'll grow out of it.

Yer arse in a band box, *you're talking nonsense*

Bob: Them granchilder of mine make some blinkin' noise.

Charlie: Runnin' about the whole time, I suppose.

Bob: An' listenin' to that oul headbangin' music.

Charlie: That stuff would go through ye, wouldn' it?

Bob: It's just noise, that's what it is - just noise.

Charlie: They say bangin' the head to that stuff helps the circulation.

Bob: Catch yerself on, ye clart.

Charlie: I'm tellin' ye, Doctor Jones told me.

Bob: Och, here, yer arse in a band box.

As wild as a mountain goat

Bob: The cub got the nose pierced.

Charlie: Get-away-a-that. He did not.

Bob: Aye, he's a ring hangin' from it.

Charlie: Does he think he's goin' to the mart or what?

Bob: He wouldn' look out of place, that's the truth.

Charlie: Sure they're stickin' all kinds of things into themselves now. Aren't ye glad it's only his nose an' not that tongue of his.

Bob: That boy's as wild as a mountain goat.

He thinks the sun came up just to hear him crow

Bob: The wife got me a record for Christmas.

Charlie: That was fierce good of her.

Bob: U2.

Charlie: Me too, what? She got me one, too?

Bob: No, that's the name of the band.

Charlie: An' what kind of stuff do they do?

Bob: They play the guitar an' jump about.

Charlie: Och aye, that's yer man, Bonehead.

Bob: Aye, somehin' like that. Wears the sunglasses, even indurs.

Charlie: He'd be hard to put up with.

Bob: He thinks the sun came up just to hear him crow.

Sendin' a cub on a man's errand

Bob: I'll put that cub from next dur into next week when I get him.

Charlie: The young buck? Has he been actin' the cod again?

Bob: I asked him to watter the plants an' he's gone an' soaked the clothes on the line too.

Charlie: Yer Barbara will go mad.

Bob: What's wrong with these young ones?

Charlie: They can do nohin' right, that's the truth.

Bob: That's what I get for sendin' a cub on a man's errand.

Let sleepin' dogs lie

Bob: Japers, we could hear that wife of yers squealin' from our house.

Charlie: She's been on that phone roarin' at the wee lassie that cuts her hair all mornin'.

Bob: The wife says she made a real mess of it – is that right?

Charlie: Oh aye, she put a bowl on her head an' cut round it.

Bob: Get away. What's she lookin' like now?

Charlie: Like a man, that's what.

Bob: She should claim, I'm tellin' ye.

Charlie: Here, shhhhhh, she's comin', say nohin'.

Bob: Surely, we'll let sleepin' dogs lie.

Charlie: Here Dot, are ye all sorted?

Quare gunk, *a terrible shock*

Bob: The cub is lookin' to move out of the house.

Charlie: He is not, an' what would he want to do that for?

Bob: Him an' that lassie he's courtin' are lookin' a place of their own.

Charlie: An' has he a ring on her finger or what's the story?

Bob: Not at all, he'll not get married, not that one.

Charlie: An' he wants to move out? His mother will go spare!

Bob: Ye're right she will, he hasn' told her yet.

Charlie: There'll be some row when he does.

Bob: I better make sure I'm feedin' the cattle - I'll not be listenin' to thon.

Charlie: He'll get a quare gunk.

Bits an' bobs

Bob: The wife carries some stuff in that handbag of hers.

Charlie: Mine would be the same, everyhin' but the kitchen sink.

Bob: When we first met she only carried her purse an' glasses.

Charlie: Now I suppose she's cards an' keys an every buckin' thing.

Bob: An' a brush for the hair, too, in case it turns into a wind bush.

Charlie: No need for half the stuff, I'd say.

Bob: Not at all, sure all I need is me boots an' me cap.

Charlie: Right ye are - no need to be carryin' all them bits an' bobs.

Header, *someone lacking any common sense; someone who's a bit wild*

Bob: I mind the times the granchilder used to come to see the cows bein' milked.

Charlie: An' do they not any more?

Bob: Not at all - they're out now to all hours, runnin' the roads.

Charlie: They're all growin' up fast, ye see.

Bob: If that cub of mine was any good he'd have them in bed before *UTV Live* came on.

Charlie: I am sure he tries his best, the same boy.

Bob: Not at all, that cub is a header.

Nine o'clock an' not a child washed

Bob: How long is yer Gary away for then?

Charlie: Him an' Joanne'll not be back until Sunday night.

Bob: An' ye have the grandchilder till then?

Charlie: We do - an' I haven't had a minute's pace all day.

Bob: Ye'd never be done, that's the truth.

Charlie: They do some runnin' about when they're that age.

Bob: An' yappin', they do some yappin' too.

Charlie: What's the right time there?

Bob: It's about nine o'clock, Charlie.

Charlie: Japers, nine o'clock an' not a child washed.

A clip 'round the ear

Bob: That cub has dog hair all over that mat.

Charlie: He has it all over thon suite of furniture as well.

Bob: Them hairs get on every buckin' thing – he has the place ruined and he knows rightly to keep the dog outside.

Charlie: Ye may get the hoover out.

Bob: If herself sees that mess I may forget about me dinner.

Charlie: Get the cub to clane it up.

Bob: I'll give him a clip 'round the ear as well, that's what I'll do.

The life of riley

Bob: That wiman of me brother's is hard to stick.

Charlie: That's the one with all the jewellery?

Bob: That's right, an' didn' pay for one bit of it herself.

Charlie: An' the muck on the face?

Bob: Aye, she wears that fake tan stuff, ye get it in a bottle.

Charlie: She looks like she's been ploughin' the whole day.

Bob: An' she got the teeth claned.

Charlie: Can she not clane her own teeth with a brush?

Bob: No, I mean, she got them painted white.

Charlie: Thon doll has the life of riley.

Dressed up to the nines

Bob: It was the grandchild's birthday yisterday.

Charlie: Which one was that?

Bob: The youngest one, Alfie.

Charlie: That likes the tractors.

Bob: Aye, an' leapin' about.

Charlie: How'd that go?

Bob: He got one of them tablets.

Charlie: What would ye be givin' a cub tablets for?

Bob: No, a tablet - one of them 'puters ye carry about.

Charlie: I would have got an orange when I was his age.

Bob: An' he was dressed up to the nines, too. He looked like a new pin.

Heart of corn, *a warm, caring heart*

~~~~~~

Bob: I was fierce sorry to hear about that uncle of yers.

Charlie: Och, sure these things happen. It was the drink that kilt him.

Bob: Was he a wile man for the sauce?

Charlie: No, Noel who owns the pub knocked him down at The Cross.

Bob: The wife says he was a decent fella, loved her wheaten scones.

Charlie: He did, an' he would have done anyhin' for ye.

Bob: A heart of corn, just.

Courtin', *old-fashioned term for dating; going out with*

~~~~~~

Bob: Me an' herself are married forty-five years the day.

Charlie: That's some length of time to be stuck with ye.

Bob: Sure she'd be lost without me.

Charlie: I'd say she's tried losin' ye.

Bob: Do ye know where I proposed?

Charlie: At the pictures, I suppose?

Bob: No, we were eatin' chips in the car, an' I said 'Barbara, will ye marry me?' An' she said 'I will.'

Charlie: An' were ye long with her at that stage?

Bob: We'd only been courtin' for a month an' a half. We didn' hang about in them days.

The sally rod, *a thin, wooden stick, often made of willow*

Bob: The cub was a bad rascal when he was a child.

Charlie: Up to all sorts, I suppose.

Bob: Ye name it, he did it, that's the truth.

Charlie: That's childer for ye.

Bob: I remember one time he stuck a banana up the exhaust of me car.

Charlie: Get-away-a-that!

Bob: Oh aye, an' he was laughin' his head off.

Charlie: An' what did ye do?

Bob: I took the sally rod to his backside, that's what I did.

Skite, *a slap*

Bob: There was some handlin' here last night.

Charlie: Did the cows get out on ye again?

Bob: No, worser. That cub of mine reversed the van into the greenhouse.

Charlie: Och no, much damage?

Bob: He flattened the whole thing, fluers an' all.

Charlie: An' what about the van?

Bob: She's a write-off.

Charlie: If that was me cub, I'd bust him with kicks.

Bob: Ye said it – he's not too oul for a skite.

To get the hump, *to be annoyed or upset*

Bob: Do ye know what time I hit the pilla at last night?

Charlie: Probably the same as meself, the wee small hours?

Bob: It was about one o'clock, is right, after we finished the silage.

Charlie: An' up again this mornin' at the crack of dawn.

Bob: The wife's got the hump.

Charlie: Because ye were in late?

Bob: Because I got into bed with wellies an' all on me.

Charlie: If I did that me own wife would be hoppin' mad.

Grand if nohin' falls on him, *expression indicating a lack of concern for someone else*

Bob: That was some bit of roarin' this mornin'.

Charlie: From me brother? Wasn' it? The lummox.

Bob: He was as red as a beetroot. What was wrong with him?

Charlie: He's mad because I scraped the van yisterday.

Bob: Is that all. What's he crowin' over that for?

Charlie: He's off sugar for Lent, so it's puttin' him off the head.

Bob: Japers, an' will he settle down?

Charlie: He'll be grand if nohin' falls on him.

The less ye say the better

Bob: That's the first time I ever met yer nephew.

Charlie: Is it? He's a painter an' decorator.

Bob: That's the one surely, an' him with no shirt on.

Charlie: He was probably sweatin' the bit out.

Bob: He's a fierce hairy chest.

Charlie: Doesn' he just.

Bob: Not often ye see that in this day an' age.

Charlie: Aye, sure don't they shave everyhin' off now.

Bob: That cuttie of mine says I should shave me ear hair.

Charlie: Ye shouldn' have opened yer mouth. She'll have you trimmin' that nose hair yet.

Bob: She'll have some wait. The less ye say the better.

Talk the hind leg off a donkey

Bob: That brother of mine had me on the phone till one o'clock in the mornin'.

Charlie: Was he on the sauce or what?

Bob: No, he hasn' touched a drop since before Christmas.

Charlie: What was he after?

Bob: Him an' the wife want to sell the whole house an' skedaddle.

Charlie: Where to?

Bob: Have ye ever heard of thon Benidorm place? I tell ye, that wife of his would sell the shirt off his back if she could get away with it.

Charlie: Ye were sick listenin' to him, then so?

Bob: Ah, he'd talk the hind leg off a donkey.

Actin' the maggot, *to play up; to engage in tomfoolery*

Bob: Yer nephew's back from that Belfast, I hear.

Charlie: Aye, I thought I had got rid of him.

Bob: That's awful, did he get sick of all that runnin' about or what?

Charlie: He lost the job an' him with mouths to feed.

Bob: What was he playin' at?

Charlie: Actin' the maggot, that's what.

Far-out relation, *a distant relative, not part of the immediate family*

Bob: I'm lookin' for some chape pigeons.

Charlie: What kind of pigeons are ye after?

Bob: Them ones ye can race.

Charlie: Ye need somewhere to put them.

Bob: I've a wee house for them that I made meself.

Charlie: I'll give ye a number for a man who sells them.

Bob: Is that yer man lives with all the cats?

Charlie: That's him. They sleep in the bed with him an' all.

Bob: How'd ye know a boy like that?

Charlie: He'd be a far-out relation.

Fierce good-ah-ye

Bob: I want to take ye an' the wife out for a feed.

Charlie: Och now, would ye quit.

Bob: If it wasn't for ye an' herself the dog wouldn' have been found.

Charlie: Sure it would have came home sometime.

Bob: But it was herself who found him at Father Curry's.

Charlie: It was no bother. Curry was feedin' him biscuits when she got there.

Bob: It's a wonder he didn' bite the hand off him.

Charlie: Curry or the dog?

Bob: He's some teeth on him. Here, come on now, ye both deserve a wee feed. Get that coat on ye.

Charlie: Well, that's fierce good-ah-ye, really an' truly.

Chapter Three
Runnin' the Roads

Yonder

Bob: I'm gettin' me tractor back the day, with a new set of tyres.

Charlie: That'll be some job. That's the wee Massey 135? The two-wheel drive?

Bob: Oh aye, an' she's a six-speed gearbox.

Charlie: Do ye need a hand to get her back?

Bob: Ye're all right. The son's away to lift her.

Charlie: That might be him comin' now, look.

Bob: There he is surely – that's him over yonder.

Goosed, *exhausted*

Bob: Was that ye I saw walkin' across the fields?

Charlie: Don't get me started.

Bob: What were ye at carryin' bags of shappin'?

Charlie: That buckin' tractor of mine broke down in the middle of the town.

Bob: But sure ye only bought it off yer man the other day.

Charlie: There must have been dirty diesel in the tank.

Bob: Such a blinkin' nuisance.

Charlie: I had to leave the bales of hay an' all an' walk home.

Bob: Ye should have phoned meself for a lift.

Charlie: I'd no phone with me. I'm goosed now.

Make sure ye're well lit up, *don't forget to turn on your lights*

Bob: There's a bad night for drivin'.

Charlie: That's a night to be in front of the fire.

Bob: Throw a few sticks on an' lay back in the chair.

Charlie: Shoes off.

Bob: Mug of tay an' a wee Paris bun.

Charlie: Och, but sure I've to collect that lassie of mine.

Bob: Ye have to collect her the night yet?

Charlie: Oh aye, she doesn' finish her work for another hour.

Bob: Ye may take it easy on that road.

Charlie: I'll be grand.

Bob: An' make sure ye're well lit up.

Drive her like ye're late for Mass

Bob: How many are goin' to this thing the night?

Charlie: There'd be a right lock. Yer man with the long hair is goin'.

Bob: Has he not got the mop cut yet?

Charlie: Growin' it down to his backside, says herself.

Bob: Here, what time is it now?

Charlie: Time we were collectin' the wives an' childer.

Bob: Right, drive her like ye're late for Mass.

Coddin', *joking, messing around*

Bob: The middle cub only did his drivin' test on Monday.

Charlie: Did he pass her or fail her?

Bob: He towl us he had failed an' I lost the head altogether.

Charlie: Did ye go mad, right enough?

Bob: Aye, I towl him he'd be payin' the buckin' resit himself.

Charlie: An' what did he say to that?

Bob: He said he was only coddin' – he passed surely.

Charlie: He was tryin' to rise ye!

Bob: He's not too oul to get a boot in the arse.

Brutal

Bob: See them blinkin' little boy racers.

Charlie: Och, aren't they a real torture, just.

Bob: A day's work would suit them a lot better.

Charlie: Revvin' away there, keepin' everyone awake.

Bob: There's a cub about the height of yer knee, he'd be the ringleader.

Charlie: I suppose he thinks he's the man, does he?

Bob: Course he does, sittin' in his Punto, smokin'.

Charlie: Them modified cars aren't worth tuppence.

Bob: Not at all, they're brutal as could be.

Banjaxed, *broken beyond repair*

Bob: See thon tractor of mine? I can't get her goin' at all. I thought the 135 was better than that.

Charlie: Is she not movin'?

Bob: She hasn' moved an inch in a day an' a half. Thornton never had this trouble with his 135.

Charlie: Would she be out of oil or what?

Bob: I couldn' right tell ye what's wrong with her.

Charlie: Turn the key there till we see.

Bob: Ye listenin'? Nohin'. Not a whisper. She's banjaxed.

Charlie: So I see surely, there's not a kick out of her.

Bob: An' I need her for cuttin' the silage.

Charlie: Need thon? I've better for cuttin' me lawn.

In an awful way, *in a fix; troubled*

Bob: I was in a wile hurry this mornin' so I was.

Charlie: Did ye get to Doctor Wilson in time at all?

Bob: Sure, wait till ye hear, didn' that buckin' car stop on me.

Charlie: Och, no.

Bob: The wheel was flat.

Charlie: An' ye couldn' get her moved.

Bob: I couldn' even find the jack for her, high up or low down.

Charlie: Was it not in the boot?

Bob: I don't know what that cub of mine did with it when he got the lend of it.

Charlie: Sounds like ye were in an awful way. Sure, come on in, Dot's away gettin' her ears syringed.

Townie

Bob: There's a boy doesn' know how to drive, look.

Charlie: He's away in second gear, when he should be in third.

Bob: Ye'd know he wasn't from about here.

Charlie: Look at the wave of him.

Bob: Did ye see he put the whole hand up instead of the one finger?

Charlie: I did - thon boy must be a townie.

Arseways, *completely wrong*

Bob: That buckin' Road Service made some mess of the road.

Charlie: What was it they were tryin' to do anyway?

Bob: They were tryin' to stop it from floodin', but sure look at it.

Charlie: There's watter everywhere, ye'll need the wellingtons.

Bob: Ye'll need more than them, ye'll need a rowin' boat, that's the truth.

Charlie: They haven' done it proper at all then.

Bob: Indeed they have not, they've done it arseways.

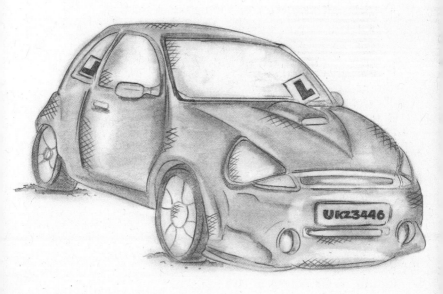

Throughother, *disorganised; untidy*

Bob: Here, didn' the police stop me when I was goin' home from the bingo.

Charlie: Whereabouts were they sittin'?

Bob: Hidin' near the bus shilter.

Charlie: But sure ye only had the one drop for the heartburn.

Bob: They were lookin' the licence an' I couldn' find it.

Charlie: I suppose ye have to take it into the station now.

Bob: I do, an' the wife's givin' me some grief about it.

Charlie: She'll be grand if nohin' falls on her.

Bob: She says it's a pity she didn' marry me brother instead, so she could be drippin' in jewellery an' fake tan too.

Charlie: Och now, ye're a bit throughother, that's all.

Desperate altogether, *very undesirable, unfortunate or difficult*

Bob: I've been on the phone to that Road Service all mornin'.

Charlie: What do ye want to talk to them for?

Bob: I nearly lost the car in a pothole opposite McDaniel's lane.

Charlie: Was it a big oul drop?

Bob: Ye could have buried a bus in it, that's the truth.

Charlie: Ye should put in a claim.

Bob: I had to get two new tyres, so I did.

Charlie: An' did ye tell them that?

Bob: Sure they haven' bothered their backside answerin' the phone.

Charlie: It's desperate altogether. An' I'm workin' all the hours God sends to pay me taxes for that!

Diabolical

Bob: Have ye settled any after the handlin' this mornin'?

Charlie: How would anyone settle after thon.

Bob: But sure it could have been worser.

Charlie: Worser? Me exhaust fell off in the middle of the town.

Bob: At least she didn' stop goin' altogether.

Charlie: I counted ten cars behind me, blowin' the horns.

Bob: That doesn' matter a damn.

Charlie: An' yer man on the bike give me the finger.

Bob: Well, there was no need for that.

Charlie: If I see him again he'll know all about it.

Bob: I'd rip the finger off him.

Charlie: The whole thing was diabolical.

Chapter Four
From the Cradle to the Grave

A tonne weight

Bob: I hear congratulations are in order.

Charlie: Och, thanks very much, Bob.

Bob: I'd shake yer hand but me own is covered in cow dung.

Charlie: Ye're all right. The lassie is on cloud nine.

Bob: Another wee babby, I'd say the wife is wile happy.

Charlie: Sure she's mad about the granchilder.

Bob: An' how's the wee cub doin' now?

Charlie: Grand, but here, he's a tonne weight.

A cub or a cuttie?

Charlie: Fair play to ye, ye're a grandfather again.

Bob: Och, I'd be well used to it now.

Charlie: Is it a cub or a cuttie?

Bob: It's a wee cuttie. Sophie Emily Eve. She has a full head of hair an' all.

Charlie: Japers, that explains yer lassie's heartburn.

Bob: We couldn' get enough bakin' soda into her.

Charlie: I'd say the Royal Victoria is some place.

Bob: 'Tis boy, they have everyhin' up there.

Charlie: Not like the day I was born.

Gansey, *a smart dress for a special occasion*

Bob: I hardly recognised that wife of yers the day.

Charlie: She had to get the face done for that christenin'.

Bob: She had a right bit of slap on surely.

Charlie: She was at it most of the mornin' an' me tryin' to eat me porridge.

Bob: Ye'd hardly know her without the wellingtons an' grape in the hand.

Charlie: I didn' even change me shoes, she put me to shame.

Bob: It's that gansey she'd on her and her hair all done. It would do ye no harm to run a comb through that wind bush of yers once in a while.

The apple didn' fall far from the tree

Bob: He's got the father's big forehead, doesn' he?

Charlie: Japers, he does ye know.

Bob: It'll be no time before he's clannin' about on that farm.

Charlie: He'll be grapin' silage, man dear, before ye know it.

Bob: He takes a fierce look at the livestock, so he does.

Charlie: Their wee heads do some movin' about at that age.

Bob: Like his own father's did when he was a cub.

Charlie: The apple didn' fall far from the tree, then so.

More fool him

Bob: I see Willy is gettin' married for a third time.

Charlie: What happened the last one?

Bob: Sure she left him for yer man that delivers the bread.

Charlie: An' who is this one now?

Bob: Some wiman he met on the 'puter.

Charlie: I'll not be goin' to no weddin', that's two toasters I bought already.

Bob: It's the day after the mara, I think.

Charlie: Well, more fool him.

Up to high doh, *under a lot of pressure; keyed up*

Bob: How's that lassie of yers this evenin'?

Charlie: She's wearin' the carpet through, that's the truth.

Bob: Marchin' up an' down, frettin', I suppose.

Charlie: Oh aye, an' on that phone givin' out to all sorts.

Bob: But sure ye only get married once.

Charlie: Unfortunately, unless ye're Willy.

Bob: An' what about himself, how's he gettin' on with writin' the speech?

Charlie: Oh, he's up to high doh, too.

Made a show of himself

Bob: Who got married?

Charlie: Ye know that Julian an' Leanne pair who sell the cement?

Bob: I do surely – Leanne's a hardy worker, wheels the barra.

Charlie: It was right good, apart from that cub of mine.

Bob: He didn' shame ye, did he?

Charlie: He had the tie round the head, an' the belly out, dancin'.

Bob: Sure nobody would have passed any remarks.

Charlie: I did, he made a right show of himself.

Howl on, *stop talking for a minute; wait a second*

Bob: Harold's gettin' married at last.

Charlie: I heard that an' him nearly seventy.

Bob: He's invited the pair of us to his stag do next month.

Charlie: At our age? Ye're pullin' me leg.

Bob: I'm tellin' ye, there's an invite up in the house. Yers'll be there when ye get home.

Charlie: An' where's he havin' it?

Bob: I think he's lookin' to go to that Amsterdam place.

Charlie: Where they sit up to all hours smokin' that wacky backy stuff? Now, just ye howl on a minute.

Janey Mac, *an exclamation of astonishment*

Bob: I was mortified at the Carsons' weddin' on Saturday.

Charlie: Did the brother make a show of himself?

Bob: I made a show of meself, to be honest with ye.

Charlie: Did ye drink one of them cocktails again?

Bob: The stomach wasn't right for weeks after I had the Fuzzy Navel the last time. So, no.

Charlie: So what?

Bob: The bride wanted a photo took with meself. An' we got the photo done. She was there, himself was there, her oul mother, too, an' me.

Charlie: An' what's wrong with that?

Bob: It was only after the wife noticed me fly was down the whole time.

Charlie: Ye were flyin' low? Janey Mac!

One more clane shirt will do him

Bob: Billy has failed an awful lot, there's not a pick on him now.

Charlie: He's been like that for a while - skin and bones, just.

Bob: An' he's stooped away over, nearly touchin' the ground.

Charlie: I doubt he wouldn' have long to go.

Bob: That's what they were sayin' in the post office.

Charlie: One more clane shirt will do him.

Goner

Bob: I was walkin' the dog there an' met oul man Grimsley.

Charlie: I hear he's not in great shape.

Bob: He has to be wheeled about everywhere now.

Charlie: There's a man who would have been fitter than the rest of us.

Bob: Ye just don't know what's 'round the corner.

Charlie: Sure it can't be long now before he goes.

Bob: That man's a goner, that's the truth.

Draw them curtains

Bob: The wife says Fat Pat from The Cross dropped dead this mornin' in the house.

Charlie: Och, no. Sure I was only chattin' him yisterday.

Bob: He was lookin' the lend of a tin of emulsion from me for the back bedroom.

Charlie: Did the heart give up or what?

Bob: Nohin' was workin' right. Once you hit a certain age, sure, everyhin' goes.

Charlie: Here, I better draw them curtains.

Dead as a durnail

Bob: Yer man with the ferrets passed this mornin'.

Charlie: Oul man McDonagh? Och, that' s too bad.

Bob: It was his sister who found him in the livin' room.

Charlie: That's the one who makes him the dinners?

Bob: That's right, the other one doesn' talk to him.

Charlie: Died with the boots on I hear.

Bob: She found him in the chair, all dressed for work, dead as a durnail.

A good run

Bob: What age was yer oul boy when he died?

Charlie: He had just turned ninety-six an' a half.

Bob: An' what happened him in the end?

Charlie: He fell off a ladder an' went bang into the greenhouse.

Bob: What was he doin' up the ladder at his age?

Charlie: He was clanin' the windies, said he couldn' see out.

Bob: An' then the ladder went from under him?

Charlie: Everyhin' went, bucket an' all.

Bob: That's a terra.

Charlie: Och, he had a good run.

Fierce quick in the end

Bob: Wasn't it a real shame about Bailey?

Charlie: They only give him a week, ye know.

Bob: An' did they say how he got it?

Charlie: He was big into lyin' in them sun bed things.

Bob: Och aye, for the tan or what?

Charlie: That right, he was an orange as could be.

Bob: All ye would have seen were the whites of his eyes.

Charlie: The wife says he went fierce quick in the end.

Pushin' up daisies

Bob: Do ye ever see Stanley about now?

Charlie: I haven' seen him this long time.

Bob: Mind he used to cycle the bicycle in all weathers.

Charlie: An' if ye dared look at him he'd swear at ye.

Bob: He had an awful dorty mouth, I mind that surely.

Charlie: An' no shoes on the feet either.

Bob: That's right, but ye'd miss seein' him about.

Charlie: I'd say he'd be pushin' up daisies by now.

Tears trippin' her

Bob: I'll not be about the day, the dog's dead.

Charlie: Och, Gizmo, the poor crater. Oul age?

Bob: I don't know right, but the mood in the house is not great.

Charlie: What about herself?

Bob: Och, she's cryin' flat out.

Charlie: Isn't that a pity.

Bob: Cryin' mornin', noon an' night.

Charlie: Ye may keep her right as best ye can.

Bob: She was in the dressmakers earlier an' the tears were trippin' her.

He was more harm to himself

Bob: Look at him, lyin' there, like butter wouldn' melt.

Charlie: He wasn't easy to put up with, thon boy.

Bob: Not at all, sure he was a wild man in his day.

Charlie: Is that right?

Bob: Oh, he would have drank a pile of stuff an' then ploughed the fields.

Charlie: An' him drunk as a skunk?

Bob: He couldn' even stand up half the time.

Charlie: He was more harm to himself, then so.

Ye goin' to the house?

Bob: I can't get over yer man poppin' the clogs like thon.

Charlie: On the toilet.

Bob: Would ye credit it?

Charlie: He was readin' the paper one minute, dead the next. The wife found him, with the trousers round the ankles.

Bob: Such a way to go.

Bob: I've often been on the toilet that long that the wife thinks I've died.

Charlie: Ye goin' to the house?

Bob: Aye, Barbara has made samwidges.

He doesn' look himself at all

Bob: God bless us an' save us, is that the time?

Charlie: That's it surely – time we were headin' away.

Bob: Well, sure, I'll see ye all at the funeral the mara, then so.

Charlie: Here, we'd better pay our respects to himself before we leave here.

Bob: I think he's just along here, in the back bedroom, beside the hot press.

Charlie: Och here, doesn' he look at pace.

Bob: Japers, he doesn' look himself at all.

It'd make ye think

Bob: He never drank or smoked his entire life, I hear.

Charlie: I heard that, an' he'd go for fierce long walks.

Bob: Oh, he would have walked over fields to get to work.

Charlie: No cars back then, ye see.

Bob: He used to wrap bailer twine round them trousers.

Charlie: No belts back then either!

Bob: Och, well at least he's up there now with herself.

Charlie: It'd make ye think.

Ye're a long time dead

Bob: There's a man dead an' not once did he leave the house.

Charlie: He spent all them years indurs?

Bob: He did. He sat at thon kitchen windie an' looked out.

Charlie: Isn't that fierce sad.

Bob: That sister of his would have brought him food the odd time.

Charlie: Life's too short for sittin' about doin' nothin'.

Bob: Well, ye're a long time dead.

Ye can't take it with ye

Bob: I am half thinkin' of buyin' one of them Walkmans.

Charlie: Ye mean one of them iProds? Me cub has one for the ears.

Bob: Aye, an iProd. I wouldn' mind listenin' to that Lisa McHugh when I am walkin' the dog.

Charlie: Them things wouldn' be too chape. Are ye sure?

Bob: I might as well - I could think of worse things to listen to.

Charlie: Like that wife of yers!

Bob: Ye said it, an' anyway, sure, ye can't take it with ye.

Ye put yer boots on in the mornin' an' ye don't know who's takin' them off in the evenin'

Bob: The church is packed to the rafters, I doubt.

Charlie: They'll have a job squeezin' them all in.

Bob: The wife went to get a packet of Polo mints an' sure she'll never get back in now.

Charlie: Don't worry, there's a speaker out the front.

Bob: I only sold this boy a sow about a fortnight ago.

Charlie: An' now he's gone.

Bob: Ye know, ye put yer boots on in the mornin' an' ye don't know who's takin' them off in the evenin'.

No age, *young*

Bob: No parent should have to bury their child.

Charlie: I agree with ye, but Ethel was seventy-two. She had a long life.

Bob: But look, it should be the mothers an' the fathers to go first.

Charlie: Who knows what Himself is thinkin' up there.

Bob: It's a quare oul handlin' when they're only young.

Charlie: Is right, look at Princess Diana.

Bob: She was no age.

Would you steal me grave as quick?

Bob: Eamonn Holmes is quare craic on that television.

Charlie: He does it well an' thon job wouldn' be too easy.

Bob: Ye always have to have somethin' to say.

Charlie: I'd never be able to keep hashin' like himself.

Bob: There he's on again look.

Charlie: Whisht till we hear what he's sayin'.

Bob: Here, ye're in me chair – would ye steal me grave as quick?

Chapter Five
Days Out

I went through him for a shortcut, *to lose one's temper with someone*

Bob: I parked the cattle trailer in that town an' got a blinkin' ticket.

Charlie: Were ye on a double yella?

Bob: I was in a loadin' bay - sure I was on me way to the mart.

Charlie: Them red coats are a curse, really an' truly.

Bob: Ye'd want to see thon boy who gave me the ticket. He looked about twelve.

Charlie: These ones are gettin' younger.

Bob: Only out of nappies.

Charlie: An' straight into these big jobs.

Bob: Not like when me an' ye were runnin' about.

Charlie: Did ye give him what for?

Bob: I did, I went through him for a shortcut.

That'll help ye in the long run

Bob: Have ye seen there's a sale on in that town?

Charlie: Would there be plenty of bargains about then?

Bob: Oh aye, I got these pair of wellies, look.

Charlie: Much?

Bob: Eight poun'.

Charlie: An' are they any good?

Bob: I've been shiverin' for days, but these boyos keep the feet warm.

Charlie: Sure what more could ye want.

Bob: I've an extra pair of socks on too. Them oul things ye get at the mart are only rubbish.

Charlie: That'll help ye in the long run.

Cat melojen, *utterly terrible; awful*

Bob: Did ye hear the post office will be closed on Wednesday?

Charlie: Why is that now?

Bob: Yer wiman's uncle dropped dead the other night.

Charlie: Dead?

Bob: As a durnail. They found him face down in the pantry.

Charlie: An' there's not a one about to keep it open?

Bob: Sure they're all goin' to the funeral.

Charlie: That's not much good to me for I've me pension to lift.

Bob: It'll be open on Thursday.

Charlie: Well, cat melojen.

Awful queue

Bob: What about the wife's neck?

Charlie: Aye, she's still got the crick in it.

Bob: Did she just wake up like that or what?

Charlie: She did, she woke up an' let out a squeal.

Bob: She must have slept crooked.

Charlie: I doubt so, but she doesn' know herself.

Bob: Ye're runnin' around for her, I suppose?

Charlie: I am, such a job gettin' her tablets.

Bob: Many in the town?

Charlie: There was an awful queue in that chemist.

The nights are fairly drawin' in, *the nights are getting darker earlier*

Bob: Ye're like a man who is ready for his bed.

Charlie: The wife had me all over that town all blinkin' day.

Bob: What were you doin' all that time?

Charlie: Gettin' measured up for a new suit.

Bob: As long as it wasn't a coffin ye'll be all right.

Charlie: Now she's lookin' to go for a walk.

Bob: Tell her to look all she wants, she'll not see much.

Charlie: That's because it's black dark an' it only seven o'clock.

Bob: Aye. The nights are fairly drawin' in.

Runnin' around like a headless chicken

Bob: Herself has sent me to buy Christmas presents.

Charlie: There's nohin' I hate more than thon.

Bob: I'd rather climb a mountain in me bare feet than go into that town.

Charlie: Especially in the mouth of Christmas.

Bob: All that standin' about waitin'.

Charlie: An' ye're never done either, she'll find more for ye to do. Runnin' around like a headless chicken, an' for what?

Bob: Don't I know it. She's lookin' for me to bring home a new pair of tights too. Them ones she has on her are all laddered an' she has to go to a WI meetin' later.

Safe home

Bob: Well, I enjoyed that day with yerself an' Birney.

Charlie: Ye need to get away from the wives now an' again.

Bob: A wee bit of pace never done a man a damn bit of harm.

Charlie: Birney fairly roared when he caught the pike.

Bob: Didn' he just, it was some brute of a thing on the rod.

Charlie: I'll leave ye to it, I've to collect herself, she's gettin' the feet sanded down again.

Bob: That'll do, then so. Safe home.

Awful blether, *a person who talks too much, and often talks nonsense*

Bob: I was gettin' groceries in the shop there on Saturday.

Charlie: That's the one on the top of the hill?

Bob: No, the one at the bottom of the hill.

Charlie: I know where ye are now, right then so.

Bob: An' who walked in, but oul man Cauldwell.

Charlie: Who's that now?

Bob: Ye know yer man, would be fierce scruffy of himself.

Charlie: Och aye, sure he's never done complainin'.

Bob: Is right. He was moanin' away cause he hit a pothole after leavin' thon wife of his to bingo.

Charlie: Sure he's an awful blether.

Anyhin' wild or wonderful?

Bob: Howya after yer trip to the Free State?

Charlie: Grand, they've some roads down there compared to here.

Bob: So I hear. All tarmac, are they?

Charlie: Oh aye, but ye have to put a few of them euros in a bucket to get through.

Bob: That's to pay for the road, ye see.

Charlie: Didn' see one pothole either.

Bob: Some difference to the buckin' roads here.

Charlie: Here, don't start me.

Bob: Anyway, anyhin' wild or wonderful with yerself?

Charlie: Not a pile, but I did hit a rabbit in Ballyshannon on the way home.

Ye didn' come up thon lough in a bubble, *you're not naive; no one's getting one over on you*

Bob: I bought a pair of wellingtons an' I hadn't them on two minutes before I brought them back.

Charlie: No good to ye?

Bob: There was a hole in the bottom of them.

Charlie: Och no.

Bob: Stepped in a puddle an' me foot was soakin'.

Charlie: An' ye kept the receipt?

Bob: I did, an' I threw them back at the cub in the shop an' got me money back.

Charlie: Here, ye didn' come up thon lough in a bubble, that's for sure.

That'll be grand

Bob: Have ye all ready for the Balmoral Show?

Charlie: I just threw a bit of red diesel into the tractor there.

Bob: I've the steel toecaps in the boot of the car, do I need them?

Charlie: Ye'd be well bringin' them with ye, Donaldson is bringin' his.

Bob: I'd say we should be leavin' about eight o'clock to bate the traffic.

Charlie: Dead on, I'll collect ye an' him from the top of Thornton's hill.

Bob: That'll be grand. It'll be the first time I've ever been in the Maze.

Have a gander

Bob: Ye still on for comin' into the bookies with me?

Charlie: Och aye, I'll put a lock of poun' on surely.

Bob: Sure the Grand National only comes once a year.

Charlie: Flash Larry is the favourite to win.

Bob: Is that right? An' is he a good-lookin' horse?

Charlie: He does well for a horse with three legs.

Bob: An' he's favourite to win, ye say?

Charlie: He is, have a gander at that newspaper till ye see.

No bother at all

Bob: Ploughin' championships in Mayo the mara - are ye goin'?

Charlie: I wouldn' mind goin' surely.

Bob: I'll give ye a lift an' yer lunch - the wife's makin' samwidges.

Charlie: Sure I might as well.

Bob: Isn't it a day out, sure, shower the oul head.

Charlie: I'd need to be back in time for milkin' though.

Bob: We'll get ye back.

Charlie: That'd be wile good of ye.

Bob: It's no bother at all.

Forty winks

Bob: Here, did ye ever think ye'd find yerself in one of these things?

Charlie: A caravan? Indeed, I did not.

Bob: There's quare comfort in it, isn't there.

Charlie: The wimen are lightin' a fire outside.

Bob: I see that, we'll cook that chicken later, then so.

Charlie: Might as well put the feet up till then an' read the paper.

Bob: I've been up since early mornin', I think I'll have forty winks.

Wee pin

Bob: Have you one of them bank cards ye put in thon thing in the wall?

Charlie: The wife sent away for one the other week an' it came the day before yisterday.

Bob: Is it any use to ye?

Charlie: Och aye, ye can use it in the shops if ye're out doin' messages.

Bob: Instead of givin' them money or what?

Charlie: That's right, ye use it at the till.

Bob: An' ye just hand it to the one behind the counter?

Charlie: That's right, ye stick it in an' then the machine'll ask ye for yer wee pin.

His head's cut, *he's unhinged*

Bob: What are all the turkeys doin' on that road?

Charlie: That Mahon boy is havin' a turkey parade at the festival.

Bob: He's paradin' turkeys? Paradin' like the Twelfth of July?

Charlie: He has to apply to the Parades Commission an' all.

Bob: He does not.

Charlie: I'm tellin' ye, he has to get the road closed.

Bob: An' how many are takin' part?

Charlie: Sixty-three. An' a rooster.

Bob: I doubt his head's cut.

I'll run ye over

Bob: There's been some walkin' done the day.

Charlie: What are yer feet like now?

Bob: Covered in blisters, that's what they're like.

Charlie: An' was it worth it?

Bob: Walkin' the town for a new tumble dryer? Ye must be jokin'.

Charlie: Ye'll have them shoes worn out.

Bob: They're nearly done, I have to bring them into the cobblers.

Charlie: I'm headin' in to get tay bags now, I'll run ye over.

Tell them nohin'

Bob: Do ye ever see these ones in the town with their clipboards?

Charlie: Askin' a pile of questions? I've seen them surely.

Bob: They stopped me this mornin' to see if I wanted Sky.

Charlie: Did ye tell them there's plenty of sky up there?

Bob: I told her I hardly have time to bless meself, never mind watch the television.

Charlie: They asked me one time how me bowels were doin'.

Bob: An' what did ye say?

Charlie: I just said I go regular.

Bob: See in a case like thon, tell them nohin'.

That's cat, *that's farcical; that's ridiculous*

Bob: I was in Asda the night before last; such a job gettin' the messages.

Charlie: There was a Bank Holiday in the Free State, that's probably why.

Bob: There were no queues, it was that blinkin' self-help check-out thing.

Charlie: Oh aye, where ye have to do all yerself.

Bob: The wife sent me to buy her a new pair of drawers.

Charlie: An' ye got into bother?

Bob: The oul machine wouldn' recognise the barcode.

Charlie: Did ye not call for one of them to help ye?

Bob: I did, but sure then the thing beeped on the way out an' who walked in but Father Curry, an' me carryin' a pair of drawers that ye'd fit around a bull calf.

Charlie: Japers, that's cat.

Too big for his boots

Bob: Me an' herself were in that Belfast yisterday, havin' a wee tour of the place.

Charlie: Did ye see where they built the *Titanic*?

Bob: Did surely, they're some size of cranes, aren't they, but?

Charlie: Oh aye, I wouldn' like climbin' into the cab of thon.

Bob: There was a cub givin' the tour, I'd say it was no time ago that he was in nappies.

Charlie: Straight from the school, ye'll find.

Bob: He had some lip on him, too. Hurryin' us about the whole time.

Charlie: Too big for his boots, just.

Hooley

Bob: Ye an' the wife still goin' to this barn dance?

Charlie: We are, she's usin' a trowel on that face of hers up in the bathroom.

Bob: I hear Philomena Begley is singin' at it.

Charlie: It should be good, then so.

Bob: Och, but it'll not be like the dances years ago.

Charlie: Do ye mind the Ballroom of Romance?

Bob: Many a wiman I courted in thon place. Ye'd want to have seen them.

Charlie: Watch yerself, that wife of yers is comin' through me dur.

Bob: Ah, Barbara, ye're lookin' lovely. I was just tellin' Charlie about the hooley the night.

Say nohin' till ye hear more

Bob: Herself is askin' if somethin' happened Father Curry at the county show.

Charlie: The lamb peein' on his shoe?

Bob: Is that what it was? How did he manage that, the clart?

Charlie: He was havin' his picture took an' he lifted the wee lamb up.

Bob: An' it just let all out.

Charlie: All out over his left shoe.

Bob: What happened then?

Charlie: He threw the shoe in the bin.

Bob: Lamb pee on the shoe wouldn' cost me a thought. Must tell the wife.

Charlie: Here, say nohin' till ye hear more.

Wile dear, *wildly expensive*

Bob: The cub took the granchilder away to that new swimmin' pool.

Charlie: That's the one where they charge ye by how much ye swim?

Bob: That's right, a poun' or two for every length ye do.

Charlie: That wouldn' be long addin' up.

Bob: Depends if ye're mad into the swimmin' or not.

Charlie: I don't even like lyin' in the bath too long.

Bob: Me neither, I think the cub said he paid thirty poun' or more.

Charlie: Och here now, that's wile dear.

Gormless

Bob: Ye'd want to have seen the cub that served me in the cobblers.

Charlie: Still in short trousers, I suppose.

Bob: Thon boy wouldn' have done a day's work in his life.

Charlie: An' he probably hasn' one notion what he's at in there.

Bob: He needs a good shake to wake him up so he does.

Charlie: That would tighten him surely.

Bob: He was probably on that 'puter thing the whole night, like all those childer.

Charlie: Up chattin' wimen till all hours, I bet ye any money.

Bob: I'd say so. I've never seen someone as gormless as thon.

More power to yer elbow

Bob: Met yer man on the street there, lookin' for me vote.

Charlie: Och him - I suppose he was spoutin' his usual bull.

Bob: Of course, he said he'll do this, that an' the other.

Charlie: As soon as he gets in ye'll not see him for another five years.

Bob: I told him if he didn' get off me land I'd cover him in eggs.

Charlie: Ye did not! He would have got a right shock, I'd say.

Bob: Ye'd want to have seen the runs of him.

Charlie: Well, more power to yer elbow.

Goin' like the clappers, *moving at top speed*

Bob: Time for the Donkey Derby again, can ye believe that?

Charlie: Doesn' be long comin' round each year, does it?

Bob: Who won it last year, can ye mind?

Charlie: I think it was yer man Mahon?

Bob: Och, that's right, it was him surely.

Charlie: Mind he was hangin' off the donkey over yonder.

Bob: That's right, wearin' just a cowboy hat.

Charlie: An' nohin' else, it was the free brandy that done the damage. He was throwin' it into him like there was no the mara.

Bob: Man dear, not a stitch on him an' goin' like the clappers.

Chapter Six
Clannin' about the House

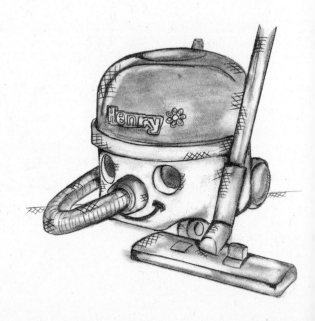

It'll do me no harm

Bob: See that street? I've been sprayin' weedkiller on it the whole day.

Charlie: The good weather brings 'em all out, ye see.

Bob: It does surely, an' such a mess they make of the place.

Charlie: Do ye wear a mask when ye're sprayin'?

Bob: I don't bother me head.

Charlie: Well ye should, that's wile dangerous ye know.

Bob: It'll do me no harm.

Tongin', *giving off; cross*

Bob: Gee, the wife's never done complainin'.

Charlie: Is she still at ye about them jobs about the house?

Bob: Oh aye, she wants new pictures of the grandchilder up on the walls.

Charlie: An' what's keepin' ye?

Bob: I've a new drill bit to get before I do anyhin'.

Charlie: Sure, do ye want the lend of mine?

Bob: She's waited six weeks; she can just wait a lock more days.

Charlie: Ye're a brave man, hi.

Bob: She'll be tongin' again, but what odds.

Whisht, *be quiet*

~~~~~~

Bob: Did you see that Stephen Nolan boy last night?

Charlie: I did not, was it any good? A shoutin' match, I suppose.

Bob: Och, shoutin' away, then he had this boy on doin' magic.

Charlie: An' was he any good?

Bob: Sure I couldn' hear a bit of it. The wife was on the phone.

Charlie: Talkin' over it.

Bob: Talkin' to the sister about curtains.

Charlie: Wouldn' that put ye mad.

Bob: I told her to whisht but I'd have been as well talkin' to meself.

Wee notion, *a fancy for; a liking for*

~~~~~~

Bob: That Christine Bleakley does be on that telly a quare lot.

Charlie: She's doin' fierce well for herself, isn't she but.

Bob: The cub thinks she's wile good-lookin'.

Charlie: Mine would be the same.

Bob: He likes that Cherie Coyle.

Charlie: I used to have a wee notion for Gloria Hunniford when I was his age. There's not a wiman about that holds a candle to our Gloria.

That'll not be straightforward

Bob: Herself is lookin' all the stuff in the kitchen moved to the livin' room.

Charlie: Is that to make room for the painter?

Bob: That's right, but sure there's a wile bit of work in carryin' all yonder, especially her dresser with all thon fancy delph. It's her pride and joy.

Charlie: I'll give ye a hand after I horn the calves.

Bob: It'd be great if ye could.

Charlie: How will ye get thon sofa through the dur?

Bob: It would want to be tipped on its side.

Charlie: That'll not be straightforward.

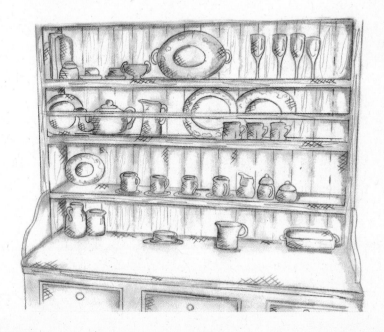

Big light, *the main light in a room; the overhead light*

Bob: The wife says to come in a minute out of the cowl.

Charlie: Are ye sure? I probably smell of cow dung.

Bob: Sure she's well used to it.

Charlie: Is that new lino on the flur?

Bob: Aye, that's there about a fortnight.

Charlie: Stops her moanin' about the dirt on the boots, I suppose.

Bob: Ye can use a mop on thon, that's why herself likes it.

Charlie: Let me get a closer look at it.

Bob: Wait till I turn on the big light.

Have a titter of wit, *have some sense*

Bob: Them big televisions are some job, aren't they?

Charlie: Aren't they, an' would ye need all them stations?

Bob: They say they have a good picture with the width of the screen an' all.

Charlie: Aye, they have that high destination or somehin'.

Bob: I told the wife I'm goin' to get one for the bedroom so I can watch *Rare Breeds* in pace.

Charlie: Did she take a look at ye?

Bob: She towl me to have a titter of wit. She says there's enough rare breeds about this house without needin' to watch them on the television too.

Bad dumour, *bad humour*

Bob: That wife of mine, I doubt she's away with it.

Charlie: Listenin' to ye, is it any wonder.

Bob: See that Valentine's Day? It sends her mad.

Charlie: Sure me wife wants to go for walks with me.

Bob: I got in yisterday an' she had lit a pile of candles.

Charlie: Was the power off?

Bob: No, she was tryin' to be romantic.

Charlie: Tell me no more.

Bob: Well, I told her to blow them out an' turn the light on.

Charlie: An' what did she say?

Bob: She's been in bad dumour ever since. She even threw the heel of the loaf at me this mornin'.

Gettin' on me wick, *getting on my nerves*

Bob: That lassie of mine got a kitchen table from Argos or somewhere.

Charlie: Oh aye, one of them ones ye have to build yerself?

Bob: That's right. Such a handlin' of a thing, a nightmare just.

Charlie: Would there be much work in the like of thon?

Bob: Ye're never done clannin' about with instructions an' wee screws no size.

Charlie: I'd say ye'd do a fair bit of footerin'.

Bob: An' could I find the Allen key.

Charlie: Have ye it done yet?

Bob: Not at all - it's gettin' on me wick.

I'll meet meself comin', *an expression indicating that a person is very busy or overstretched*

Bob: Do ye like me lawn? I must have walked ten miles cuttin' thon.

Charlie: Ye have it lookin' well - was that the first cut the year?

Bob: That's right, first cut the year, boy.

Charlie: An' ye took a strimmer to them weeds an' all.

Bob: I did surely, I was at it from about eight o'clock this mornin'.

Charlie: Ye were early on the go.

Bob: I am that busy all day that I'll meet meself comin'.

Oul hames, *a mess*

Bob: I had to get the wife to sew me good trousers earlier.

Charlie: What do ye need them for?

Bob: Paddy's remains are comin' home the night.

Charlie: Och, that's right, sure I forgot about that.

Bob: Aye, an' there was some size of hole on the knee of me trousers.

Charlie: How'd that happen?

Bob: Didn' I hunk it on an oul thorn bush.

Charlie: Did she do a good job?

Bob: She couldn' see a thing - she sat on her glasses yisterday, so she did.

Charlie: Blind as a bat, then so.

Bob: She made a real oul hames of the whole thing.

Ragin'

Bob: Came home yisterday after shearin' the sheep an' wanted a wash.

Charlie: I did the exact same, an' had a wash down at the sink, just.

Bob: With just a face cloth under the arms?

Charlie: An' a bar of soap.

Bob: See, I didn' even have that. The watter was stone cold.

Charlie: Did ye not put the pump on?

Bob: The whole thing has stopped goin' altogether.

Charlie: Ye can't have that.

Bob: Another thing to blinkin' sort out. I'm ragin'.

Charlie: I'll get the cub to take a look when he's done atein'.

Such a bit of carryin' on, *a hullaballoo*

Bob: I slept on me arm last night.

Charlie: That's not nice, I've done that before.

Bob: I thought I was dyin', to tell ye the truth.

Charlie: Did the wife do much to help?

Bob: Not at all, she was lyin' there like a sow.

Charlie: It usually goes away if ye rub it.

Bob: I went to take a mouthful of watter an' dropped the glass.

Charlie: Och no.

Bob: Wet the pyjama bottoms on meself.

Charlie: Such a bit of carryin' on.

Fed up

Bob: That house of mine is fallin' down with the young lassie's bits an' bobs.

Charlie: Is she still stayin' with yerselves, then so?

Bob: Aye, sure they still haven' fixed her ceilin' after it fell in.

Charlie: Do ye not like havin' her back in the house then?

Bob: I do, but she spends too long in that bathroom paintin' that face.

Charlie: That's the wimen for ye.

Bob: It would be all right if I didn' put the immersion on for her every mornin'.

Charlie: I am sure she likes seein' her oul boy.

Bob: I don't know – all I know is I am fed up waitin' to use the toilet.

Ye'll not feel the benefit of it

Bob: Do ye like me new coat?

Charlie: That's some job. How much did that set ye back?

Bob: Ah, the wife got it for me for me birthday.

Charlie: It suits ye, so it does.

Bob: It's right warm, too. Feel that.

Charlie: That's a good bit of linin' that.

Bob: An' comfortable, too.

Charlie: Are ye not goin' to take it off in the house?

Bob: I was goin' to keep it on for a bit.

Charlie: Watch, or ye'll not feel the benefit of it when ye go out.

It's a real curse of a thing

Bob: See that boiler of ours, ye have to time everyhin'.

Charlie: Och, aye, so that it comes on when ye want it on?

Bob: That's right, herself wants it to go on the middle of the night.

Charlie: Sure, what good is that to ye when ye're asleep?

Bob: She wants it warm when she gets up to make the porridge.

Charlie: An' have ye it all set?

Bob: Sure I can't see the buckin' thing to time it.

Charlie: They make ye squint at everyhin' now.

Damn nuisance

~~~~~~

Bob: The wife got me one of them ice phones for Christmas.

Charlie: What would that be when it's at home?

Bob: It's one of them things ye have to touch the screen with yer finger.

Charlie: An' the writin' would be no size, I'd say.

Bob: Is right, an' sure nohin' works half the time.

Charlie: Is it any wonder yer eyes are bucked then.

Bob: The eyesight's not what it used to be, ye know.

Charlie: I think I need glasses, meself.

Bob: I'd be goin' the same way.

Charlie: Such a damn nuisance.

Bob: It's a real curse of a thing.

I can still find the draught

Bob: I haven' warmed all day, not once.

Charlie: I wouldn' dare put me nose outside in thon.

Bob: Isn't it a terra an' them double-glazed windies an' all.

Charlie: Ye want a wee sheet of newspaper against the dur.

Bob: I put down coats, pullovers, ye name it. The wife goes mad.

Charlie: The cowl must try yer patience.

Bob: Does. Ye'd feel it on yer bones.

Charlie: Ye need one of them wee standalone haters.

Bob: Is right. Sure even now I can still find the draught.

Wouldn' be a pile of good

Bob: The wife's off with that friend of hers to the Isle of Man.

Charlie: Hi boy, that's some length away.

Bob: They're away on a bus, would ye believe.

Charlie: An' ye're left holdin' the fort.

Bob: The whole shebang; cookin', clanin', the whole damn lot.

Charlie: How are ye usin' the washin' machine?

Bob: Grand, but thon thing is fallin' apart.

Charlie: That's not much help to ye.

Bob: It wouldn' be a pile of good. I've only one pair of long johns to do me till she comes back.

Does me head in

Bob: That cub of mine needs his arse kicked into next week.

Charlie: He hasn' driven the mini digger into the side of the house again?

Bob: He's done somehin' even worser. He let them cows out on purpose.

Charlie: Och, not on purpose?

Bob: I'm tellin' ye, he did it out of pure badness.

Charlie: An' where'd they end up?

Bob: In Mrs Thornton's garden. Ate her plants an' everyhin'.

Charlie: Ye'd want to give him a quare skite.

Bob: He does me head in.

Does some hashin', *does some chatting; talks all the time*

Bob: Do ye ever listen to that Hugo Duncan on the radio?

Charlie: I would, I'd listen to him when I'm in for a drop of tay.

Bob: The wee man from Strabane he calls himself.

Charlie: He'd play a right bit of that country music.

Bob: That'd be the type of stuff I'd have courted to years ago.

Charlie: In the dance halls? Didn' I do a bit of that meself.

Bob: He would do a bit of talkin', that Hugo. Never stops.

Charlie: Ye're right there – he does some hashin'.

Lost the run of himself

Bob: There's a boy there is hard to listen to.

Charlie: Who?

Bob: Yer man who keeps the goats.

Charlie: He hasn' been right since he caught that thing on the ear.

Bob: That's right, off the phone in the phone box by The Cross?

Charlie: That's the one. The whole ear oozed for a lock of days.

Bob: An' now he doesn' know what he's at.

Charlie: He thought he was dyin' so he lost the plot altogether.

Bob: Didn' he leave the wife an' all?

Charlie: He did. An' he took the television with him.

Bob: He's just lost the run of himself, then so.

Some neck on him, *some cheek*

Bob: Grimsley was at the dur again.

Charlie: What did he want this time?

Bob: He was lookin' the lend of the shovel.

Charlie: An' I hope ye told him where to go.

Bob: I did, I told him if he didn' get off me street I'd kick his arse into next week

Charlie: An' right ye were, after what he done.

Bob: Ye said it. The last time he got me shovel he broke the shaft of it.

Charlie: He's some neck on him.

No flies on ye, *street smart; you don't let the grass grow*

Bob: That van pulled up on the street yisterday.

Charlie: Boys sellin' stuff, I suppose.

Bob: Aye, they wanted me to buy a pair of steel toe-caps.

Charlie: Have ye seen them about before?

Bob: I heard about them boys, that's enough.

Charlie: Did it take ye long to get rid of them?

Bob: I told them what they could do with their boots an' they left.

Charlie: No flies on ye.

Boys a dear, *an expression of amazement or astonishment*

Bob: Here, what do ye think of this?

Charlie: What kind of thing is that?

Bob: It's one of them Henry Hoovers.

Charlie: Is there any need for it to be smilin' at ye.

Bob: That's part of it: I bought it for herself for her birthday.

Charlie: How much did that sting ye?

Bob: There's the receipt, look. I left it about so she could see it.

Charlie: Can you claim VAT back on thon?

Bob: I don't think ye can.

Charlie: Boys a dear.

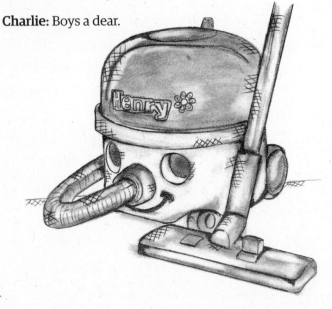

Divil the bit, *that's nonsense*

Bob: Had the television licence ones at the dur last night.

Charlie: Did ye let them in?

Bob: Indeed I did not. I turned the light off an' hid under the kitchen table.

Charlie: That's the right thing to do: imagine payin' for thon hape of dung.

Bob: Sure it's all repeats. I'd rather watch me cows chewin' the cud.

Charlie: I hear they can fine ye now if ye don't pay up.

Bob: Och now, divil the bit.

That's the truth

Bob: That's the second time this month the council didn' collect me blue bin an' them hashin' about recyclin' all the damn time.

Charlie: Do they keep forgettin' about ye or what?

Bob: They must do but they don't forget to take the rates off me.

Charlie: If ye lived in the middle of the town it would be a different story.

Bob: Is right - that's what I get for livin' in the sticks.

Charlie: As soon as nine o'clock comes, ye get on that phone.

Bob: They'll not know what hit them, that's the truth.

Does me head in, *infuriates me*

Bob: Have ye seen the colour of me watter?

Charlie: Japers, it's as yella as a duck's arse.

Bob: I've told the Watter Board about it more times.

Charlie: An' are they goin' to sort it out? Sure ye couldn' drink thon.

Bob: I'm hopin' the wife takes a sip – I might get a bit of pace then.

Charlie: I've a number in the house for the man in charge.

Bob: Sure I was on the phone for three-quarters of an hour earlier.

Charlie: Japers, that would do me head in.

I don't boil me cabbage twice, *I won't tell you twice; I won't repeat myself*

Bob: I had a boy on the phone yisterday, talkin' an' askin' me things.

Charlie: One of them oul nuisance calls, was it?

Bob: He was askin' me if I ever bought a pie or somehin'.

Charlie: A pie? Ye mean PPI?

Bob: Aye, that's the boyo. He was goin' on an' on for ages.

Charlie: An' what did ye say to him?

Bob: I towl him to stop wastin' me blinkin' time.

Charlie: Anybody rings ye like thon, just put the phone down.

Bob: He'll know not to ring here again. I don't boil me cabbage twice.

Huffin'

Bob: Ah, here. Didn' I forget the wife's birthday.

Charlie: Och now, an' how long have ye two been married?

Bob: Too long. She's not happy at all.

Charlie: Ye may buy her a thing of fluers.

Bob: I'd say it's probably too late for even that.

Charlie: Is she givin' out much?

Bob: She's a face on her would turn milk sour.

Charlie: Ye may do somehin' quick.

Bob: I put the jar in the bed for her.

Charlie: An' how'd that go down?

Bob: She's still huffin'.

Vexed

Bob: Have ye seen me tomata plants?

Charlie: Naw, I haven' been outside the day yet.

Bob: Go an' take a look at 'em.

Charlie: What's happened. Have they wilted or what?

Bob: There'll all dead, every one of 'em.

Charlie: They are not. That's a terra, that is.

Bob: They'd want to be all dumped now.

Charlie: That would break me heart.

Bob: Me heart is broken surely; I doted over me tomata plants.

Charlie: Ye may grow more then.

Bob: Sure I know, but I'm still wile vexed about it.

That's a hundred, *that's a hundred per cent, that's great*

Bob: Can I get the lend of your sledge?

Charlie: What do ye want it for?

Bob: There's a wall over there that needs flattened.

Charlie: Ye're not takin' down the whole wall, are ye?

Bob: I am surely, that's why I need yer sledge.

Charlie: The wife's usin' it to do up the bathroom till then.

Bob: What are ye gettin' done to it?

Charlie: She wants a new sink in an' one of them walk in showers.

Bob: Has she tore the bath out an' all?

Charlie: Oh aye, the bath's gone. The place is like a bomb hit it.

Bob: It'll be some job when it's done.

Charlie: I could give ye the sledge at the weekend, then so.

Bob: That's a hundred.

Flat to the mat, *extremely busy*

Bob: Here, are ye about on Tuesday?

Charlie: Why, what's Tuesday?

Bob: I need a hand to cut thon hedge. The wife never shuts up about it.

Charlie: I would, but I've a new washin' machine to plumb for the sister this three weeks.

Bob: Sure that'll not take ye long.

Charlie: I know, but then she wants the oul one dumped. I'll be away all day.

Bob: I'll have to ask the cub then I suppose.

Charlie: I'd help ye surely, but I am flat to the mat.

Chapter Seven
Health and Wealth

Black an' blue

Bob: What about Father Curry this mornin'? He was in some shape.

Charlie: He wasn' the best - such a bit of whingin'.

Bob: He hasn' been right since he fell off thon ladder.

Charlie: What was he doin' up that ladder, the cod?

Bob: He was tryin' to get Mrs McCabe's cat down from the ledge.

Charlie: He must have had some fall.

Bob: The ladder went from under him. He's a lump on that ankle the size of a house.

Charlie: Is it big, right enough?

Bob: 'Tis boy, an' he's black an' blue.

As tight as could be

Bob: It was only a matter of time before they buried yer man.

Charlie: Is right, it's a wonder they even found him in there.

Bob: He was hidden away in that house most of his life.

Charlie: Never went out, always lay in that bed, readin' the paper.

Bob: Never put on a light either, or a bit of hate, nohin'.

Charlie: What kind of life was that?

Bob: Sure ye know yerself, he was as tight as could be.

Ye'll catch yer death

Bob: Ye're all wet – is it pourin' out there?

Charlie: It is, boy: the watter is runnin' down me back.

Bob: Did ye catch the mouse ye were after?

Charlie: I ran around the whole place after him an' got him in the meal bag.

Bob: Japers, he was hungry, ye see.

Charlie: There must be half a dozen out there now.

Bob: Ye have a job on yer hands.

Charlie: Am away out again an' it's still rainin'.

Bob: Och here, ye'll catch yer death.

Failed away to nohin', *wasted away*

Bob: Did Father Curry say how long Ledwith has left?

Charlie: Och, I wouldn' think he'd have too long now.

Bob: There's hardly a pick on him.

Charlie: He hasn' been able to ate a thing for weeks, no appetite or damn all.

Bob: An' thon boy would have been a big ater in his day.

Charlie: He would have threw the fist on the table for seconds.

Bob: I hardly knew it was him in that hospital.

Charlie: I know – he's failed away to nohin'.

Nerves are gone, *feeling jittery or anxious, often because of a specific event; suffering from a nervous disposition*

Bob: See them granchilder of mine an' them bangers.

Charlie: That's all the young ones do at Hallowe'en, sure.

Bob: We can't get a minute's pace with them.

Charlie: There's some rip off them when they go up, isn't there?

Bob: They're lettin' them off all the time, in bins an' everyhin'.

Charlie: Just make sure ye keep that dog in the house.

Bob: The wife's nerves are gone. She's hid under thon kitchen table more times, that's the truth.

She'd be hard to shoe, *she's high maintenance; she'd be hard to keep in the manner to which she's accustomed*

Bob: That was some weddin' of them two young things.

Charlie: Sure they're only childer.

Bob: He's a right fella but I'm not so sure about Lady Muck.

Charlie: She likes the doh-ray-me a bit too much.

Bob: She had some amount of jewels around that throat.

Charlie: She got the eyes done too – with his money.

Bob: No need for the glasses, then so, isn't it tellin' her.

Charlie: Oh, she'd be hard to shoe.

Dyin' on me feet

Charlie: Here, Bob, didn' expect to see ye up the town.

Bob: The wife has me standin' sellin' these here raffle tickets all day.

Charlie: What are ye sellin' them for?

Bob: The cuttie an' a lock of lassies are away to Africa to build a hut.

Charlie: Like a mud hut or what?

Bob: Some place for the childer to stand under if it's teemin'.

Charlie: That would be some job out there surely.

Bob: I need to get them tickets sold first.

Charlie: Have ye been out long?

Bob: About an hour an' I'm dyin' on me feet.

The price of thon is a terra, *the price of that is ferocious*

Bob: There's some money spent on weddins these days, isn't there but?

Charlie: That's right, Bob, some money spent surely.

Bob: An' for just one blinkin' day.

Charlie: Ye could buy a new ride-on for the price Beryl in the fishmongers is payin' to get married to that man of hers.

Bob: An' they've a house ye could fit the whole lot of us in.

Charlie: I heard that, two toilets an' all fitted, one upstairs an' one down.

Bob: It's a wonder they've any money left after that weddin'.

Charlie: Och here, the price of thon is a terra.

Clane mad, *incandescent with rage*

Bob: Did ye hear about Jacqueline?

Charlie: That's yer wife's sister?

Bob: Aye, she's the one with the bad angina an' diabeetus.

Charlie: Surely - I was chattin' to her down the town on Tuesday.

Bob: They've stopped her DLA.

Charlie: They have not.

Bob: Took the whole lot off her. Car an' all.

Charlie: An' her can't walk the length of herself.

Bob: She's to go for an assessment now.

Charlie: An' the amount of ones on it an' they don't need it.

Bob: The wife's goin' clane mad about it.

Kilt with pains, *to have agonising pains*

Bob: See that leg of mine, do ye see that?

Charlie: Would ye look at that – it's swelled up like a balloon.

Bob: Me other leg is the same. That's what I get for spreadin' dung all day yisterday.

Charlie: An' what about that back of yers? Any better?

Bob: It's a buckin' nuisance, that's the truth.

Charlie: An' ye hurted it when ye fell off thon ladder?

Bob: That's right, the wife had to help me up off the groun'. I'm kilt with pains.

Charlie: Aren't ye lucky she got ye before it rained.

There must be somehin' goin', *there's a bug going around*

Bob: How are ye the day?

Charlie: Och, sure, ye know.

Bob: Coughin' an' splutterin'?

Charlie: That's right, an' the sweat is rollin' off me.

Bob: I'd be the same.

Charlie: What are ye like goin' to the toilet?

Bob: I've them oul kidney stones. It's like passin' razor blades, that's the truth.

Charlie: I'm up an' down to thon toilet the whole night. The wife's goin' mad.

Bob: There must be somehin' goin'.

I'm not near well

Bob: I doubt I've got that dorty bug.

Charlie: Are ye findin' it hard to swalla?

Bob: The throat is red raw, so it is. I'm not near well.

Charlie: Have ye been takin' anyhin' for it?

Bob: The wife gave me a spoonful of stuff earlier.

Charlie: Ye need to put yer head in a basin of hot watter with a towel over ye an' sniff.

Bob: What will that do to me?

Charlie: Clears that oul nose of yers. Helps ye to breathe.

Bob: Och, yer arse, it'll make me nose run, that's what it'll do.

That dose is goin' round

Bob: Me head is poundin'.

Charlie: Yer head is poundin'? Me legs are like jelly.

Bob: Are ye wake, right enough?

Charlie: I am wake. I better not stand in case I fall down.

Bob: Yer man Thornton fell over last night in church.

Charlie: That useless lump. It's them special shoes for his flat feet, I told him to stop wearin' them out of the house.

Bob: Aye, fell straight over with a bang.

Charlie: Is he sick too?

Bob: He was splutterin' through the whole service. Father Curry had to stop twice.

Charlie: Japers, that dose is goin' round, then so.

Stiff as a boord

Bob: I sat in thon chair boy an' I watched that rally the whole evenin'.

Charlie: Did yer man Hamilton win again?

Bob: Just about; he was gettin' it tight in that last lap, though.

Charlie: Flyin', I suppose.

Bob: Flyin' surely.

Charlie: It would have been good, I'd say.

Bob: It was surely - them yokes can go some speed.

Charlie: Ye'd hardly see them.

Bob: I tell ye what, though, I am stiff as a boord now.

Gammy leg, *injured or sore leg*

Bob: Ye should have seen Mrs O'Doherty comin' out of the post office this mornin'.

Charlie: That's the policeman's wife?

Bob: Aye, the big tall thing. Drives the Ka.

Charlie: Wasn't she in the Royal for a week or two?

Bob: She was, an' she still wouldn' be a hundred.

Charlie: I heard that all right.

Bob: She's a lump on thon forehead the size of an orange.

Charlie: An' does she still have the problem with them veins?

Bob: Oh aye, she has a gammy leg surely.

Failed a sight, *gone downhill rapidly (referring to health)*

Bob: Japers, Thornton's not lookin' himself at all.

Charlie: He had that accident with the plough, do ye mind?

Bob: That's right, an' he lost a couple of fingers.

Charlie: He's not able to lift the shovel now.

Bob: Isn't it a terra how easy it can happen.

Charlie: Ye know, I don't think he's been right since.

Bob: Not at all, an' sure then the hearin' went.

Charlie: An' he's pains in his joints, too.

Bob: Och, he's failed a sight.

Bad dose, *unpleasant illness, often flu*

Bob: Me eyes have been streamin' the whole day.

Charlie: I'm the same. It looks like I've been cryin'.

Bob: Are ye sneezin' full time, too?

Charlie: I am, an' I am wile dizzy.

Bob: I've a temperature, too; the head's on fire.

Charlie: I don't even have the strength to bless meself.

Bob: Throw a hot whiskey intil ye an' ye'll be grand.

Charlie: I doubt I have a bad dose.

Me back is wringin'

Bob: I've been cuttin' turf in the bog the whole day.

Charlie: The whole day? Did ye not get a break at all?

Bob: I stopped for a samwidge an' that was about it.

Charlie: An' have ye all done now or would there be more to do?

Bob: There'd be a bit more, all right, but Thornton said he'd give me a hand.

Charlie: Ye'd want to bring a mineral with ye, an' drink plenty.

Bob: Don't I know it, ye'd need it surely. Me back is wringin'.

The sheet was stickin' to me

Bob: Have ye ever had a wile bad chill in the kidneys?

Charlie: Och, aye. I've had it plenty of times over the years.

Bob: I've had it this fortnight an' it's a wile buckin' thing to move.

Charlie: Would yer head be boilin'?

Bob: One minute I'm sweatin', the next I'm shiverin'.

Charlie: It's no joke, that's the truth.

Bob: An' last night I had the wife's head turned.

Charlie: Was she givin' out?

Bob: She was, I woke up an' the sheet was stickin' to the pair of us.

Middlin'

~~~~~~

Bob: I doubt I may have got that oul sunstroke.

Charlie: That's what ye get for stayin' out for so long.

Bob: I was out all day mixin' cement in a bucket.

Charlie: An' the sun was splittin' the stones, I suppose.

Bob: It was an' sure didn' I go out without the cap.

Charlie: Ye'd need a cap on the head a day like that.

Bob: Sure I know. What 'bout yerself, howya?

Charlie: Och middlin', apart from this oul arm, I must a sprained it wrestlin' with that bull calf of mine yisterday.

Quern tired, *utterly exhausted*

~~~~~~

Bob: I can't wait to get these boots off me.

Charlie: I'm the same – I'm goin' to lie in that bath the whole night.

Bob: I'll put me feet in the wife's foot spa thing. It's some job to relax ye.

Charlie: That's that oul thing where the watter moves?

Bob: Oh aye, them bubbles are suppose to ease the feet.

Charlie: I need somehin' after ploughin' up that mountain all day.

Bob: Here, we'll sleep well the night, that's for sure.

Charlie: Right ye are, I am quern tired.

Didn' get a wink

Bob: I done some tossin' an' turnin' last night in that bed.

Charlie: What was keepin' ye awake?

Bob: That buckin' dog never shut his mouth.

Charlie: Was there someone out on the street or what?

Bob: I think he has a notion of next dur's dog, he never shut up outside the back dur.

Charlie: That'd be hard to listen to.

Bob: Between him an' the wife, me head is turned.

Charlie: What's wrong with herself?

Bob: She snored the whole night through.

Charlie: Did ye get a lock of hours at least?

Bob: Not at all - I didn' get a wink.

Poor crater, *poor thing*

Bob: Do ye see that Grimsley boy these days at all?

Charlie: I saw him walkin' the roads the other day, with the dog beside him.

Bob: An' how was he lookin'?

Charlie: He's aged a terra. Ye'd hardly know him, draggin' the leg behind him.

Bob: He'd be on a pile of tablets, too. I'd say ye could fill a chemist's shop with them.

Charlie: Ye could surely, an' he's still on them crutches.

Bob: The wife says he wears an eye patch, as well.

Charlie: The poor crater.

I haven' one notion, *I haven't a clue*

Bob: It was some craic earlier – the wife was helpin' me move the cattle.

Charlie: An' her wouldn' be fond of the things at all.

Bob: Is right, an' then sure didn' she hurt her shoulder.

Charlie: I'd say there was some squealin' done.

Bob: Would ye quit, she never done tongin' the whole evenin'.

Charlie: How'd she do it?

Bob: She pulled a muscle tryin' to lead the big cow on a rope into me trailer.

Charlie: How is she now?

Bob: I got out of that house as quick as I could, so I haven' one notion. But the cow's fine.

Worser

Bob: What about yer Tommy? Is he well?

Charlie: Sure he got the toe off last week.

Bob: What was wrong with it?

Charlie: Och, he let it go bad.

Bob: How did he do that?

Charlie: He stood on a rusty nail; went right up his welly. He didn' even get it looked at.

Bob: An' he had to get the whole toe off?

Charlie: The whole toe surely.

Bob: What would he be like now?

Charlie: He can't get up or down the stairs.

Bob: Tell him I was askin' about him.

Charlie: I will, but I doubt he's gettin' worser.

Not a word about it, *don't be ridiculous; don't say a word more about it*

Bob: Have ye got the flu injection yet?

Charlie: That thing would only make ye drop.

Bob: Not at all, me own doctor says ye need it.

Charlie: I know a boy who fell like a stone after gettin' thon.

Bob: Ye're not suppose to ate before it so he was probably just wake.

Charlie: Och, I doubt I'll give it a miss.

Bob: Ye'll be six feet under by January if ye don't get it, I'm tellin' ye.

Charlie: Not a word about it.

Me back is broke

Bob: Where does it hurt ye?

Charlie: All over me back.

Bob: The middle of yer back or where?

Charlie: From me backside up.

Bob: An' have ye tried any Deep Heat on it?

Charlie: There's none in the press – I looked when I got in.

Bob: Don't lie there crooked, lie straighter than that.

Charlie: It's me own fault, I was cartin' blocks around all day.

Bob: Here, I doubt I'll have to ring that wife of yers.

Charlie: Tell her me back is broke.

Ogeous handlin', *an atrocious pickle; a terrible situation*

Bob: Do ye mind the time Corrigan had the bad tooth?

Charlie: I do, sure Thornton pulled it out with a bit of bailer twine.

Bob: That's right, in me kitchen, the wife went bananas.

Charlie: He let out some squeal, didn' he but?

Bob: Ye would have heard him a mile away, crowin'.

Charlie: He was a wile smoker so his oul teeth were rotten.

Bob: The kitchen was rotten, too. The wife never shut up about it for a week.

Charlie: An ogeous handlin' is right.

The whole thing's a terra, *a surprising or upsetting experience*

Bob: We were up in the hospital last night till all hours.

Charlie: Were ye havin' bother with the kidneys again?

Bob: No, it was the wife this time. Hit her head off the flur.

Charlie: The poor crater. How'd she do that?

Bob: She tripped over the cat's dish an' went flyin'.

Charlie: Och no, was it long before she was seen?

Bob: We would have been there a lock of hours anyway.

Charlie: Yonder place is a shambles of a place.

Bob: The whole thing's a terra.

Isn't it fierce, *isn't it dreadful*

Bob: Anyhin' wild or wonderful?

Charlie: Och, all grand, apart from me nose keeps bleedin'.

Bob: Do ye keep the head back when it does?

Charlie: Head goes back, bit of tissue, still no good.

Bob: Bleeds away?

Charlie: Like a tap, that's the truth. Quern annoyin'.

Bob: Ye're suppose to give it a tight squeeze.

Charlie: I've ruined two pairs of pyjama bottoms.

Bob: Have ye towl that doctor of yers?

Charlie: He's not free for a fortnight. That hospital has gone to pot.

Bob: Isn't it fierce.

One eye lookin' at ye an' the other lookin' for ye

Bob: The wife was tellin' me about yer man that cuts the grass.

Charlie: Wee Paul? He's the oddest boy ever I met.

Bob: So herself was sayin'. What's the craic with that?

Charlie: He'd spend all day on a lawn an' charge a small fortune.

Bob: An' does he take out the weeds an' all?

Charlie: Ye have to do that yerself.

Bob: That's no good to me.

Charlie: But sure he can barely see in front of him.

Bob: I hear he's cross-eyed.

Charlie: He's one eye lookin' at ye an' the other lookin' for ye.

I don't know if I'm comin' or goin'

Bob: That was some day out. I don't even want to look at me feet.

Charlie: What were ye at?

Bob: Deliverin' phone books.

Charlie: An' ye call that a day out?

Bob: Sure I stretched the legs if nohin' else.

Charlie: An' did ye get them all delivered?

Bob: To be honest, the ones I didn' do, I burnt in the back field.

Charlie: Ye did not! What if they look for them?

Bob: Sure they'll never know.

Charlie: Yer too tired to help me milk, then so.

Bob: I don't know if I'm comin' or goin'. I couldn' tell one end of a cow from the other.

Doesn' add up

Bob: Has yer winter fuel allowance arrived yet?

Charlie: Aye, it came there the other mornin' along with the phone bill.

Bob: Mine still hasn' come. Why would that be?

Charlie: Sure you know what they're like, they don't want to give ye anyhin'.

Bob: That's a joke of a thing, that. An' Thornton got his already, too.

Charlie: Ye need to phone them up an' give them what for.

Bob: Ye're right, I will. Somehin' doesn' add up at all.

What odds, *who cares*

Bob: Did ye get yerself all sorted?

Charlie: With the blue badge? Not at all.

Bob: Ye got the form last week. What's keepin' ye?

Charlie: They're lookin' for an oul photograph for it.

Bob: An' what's wrong with that?

Charlie: I haven' had me picture took since the day I got married.

Bob: Call into the chemist the next day ye're in town, sure. They'll do it.

Charlie: Och, what odds. I'll just do without.

Haven' a baldy, *haven't a clue; no idea*

Bob: That George Osbourne has some neck on him.

Charlie: Ye wouldn' like him if ye reared him.

Bob: He wouldn' know much about hard work, the same boy.

Charlie: There wouldn' be many of that crowd that knows too much.

Bob: They think they know plenty, don't they?

Charlie: They know how to take money off us, that's what.

Bob: They've clanned about with me pension more times is a terra.

Charlie: Here, they haven' a baldy, honestly.

Thick as two short planks

Bob: Have ye seen the colour of Father Curry?

Charlie: He wasn' out in the sun again, was he?

Bob: He fell asleep in the chair at the back of the church.

Charlie: Beside the graveyard? Not again.

Bob: Lyin' there with an ice cream in the hand.

Charlie: An' it melted everywhere, I suppose.

Bob: Worser – a swarm of wasps came along an' stung the face off him.

Charlie: There's a man as thick as two short planks.

Chapter Eight
Themuns

Happy as Larry

Bob: Were ye watchin' *Winnin' Streak* last night?

Charlie: I was clippin' the cat's nails all evenin', missed everyhin'.

Bob: Ye'll never guess who was on it?

Charlie: I wouldn' have a notion.

Bob: Thornton! He's been holidayin' down there all week.

Charlie: Japers, an' how did he do?

Bob: He won a Ford Ka, brand new.

Charlie: He did not! Wasn' he lucky.

Bob: His wife wanted a Micra, but he's happy as Larry.

Clift, *a foolish person*

Bob: Mrs Thompson's cub was at the dur the other night, collectin'.

Charlie: What was he collectin' for?

Bob: One of them oul whatty-ye-call-its.

Charlie: An oul raffle or what?

Bob: A raffle surely.

Charlie: An' how much was he after this time?

Bob: He was lookin' a fiver off me.

Charlie: I wouldn' give thon boy tuppence.

Bob: Did ye hear what he done last week?

Charlie: What was he at?

Bob: He put diesel in thon jeep of his instead of petrol.

Charlie: Och, no. He's nohin' but a clift.

Awful chancer

Bob: Did ye see yer man was in the paper again?

Charlie: McBride? I seen him surely.

Bob: Caught drivin' thon van of his with a broken tail-light.

Charlie: An' sure he was done last year for no tax or insurance.

Bob: Any wonder the wife upped sticks an' moved out.

Charlie: I heard she was fed up with all that carry-on.

Bob: Oh aye, sure he was sellin' red diesel most weekends.

Charlie: An' chape DVDs. I used to get John Wayne ones off him for a fiver.

Bob: He's just an awful chancer.

Quare cod, *someone who behaves in an idiotic manner*

Bob: That Bosco boy is some eejit, too.

Charlie: Isn't he. All that money an' not a bit of sense.

Bob: If he had a brain he'd be dangerous.

Charlie: Imagine gettin' involved with yer wiman.

Bob: An' her married before to yer man with the horses.

Charlie: Well there's only one reason she's with Bosco an' that's his money.

Bob: She'd be a money grabber surely.

Charlie: An' he hasn' an ounce of wit.

Bob: Not at all, he's a quare cod.

A luck penny, *a small sum given back to the purchaser for luck (usually in a transaction between two individuals)*

Bob: The wife wants a goose for Christmas.

Charlie: Where are ye goin' to get one of them from?

Bob: Oul man Cauldwell sells geese at the side of the road.

Charlie: Does he charge much? I wouldn' mind one meself.

Bob: He does, an' he wouldn' even give me a luck penny.

Charlie: I heard that about him, all right, an' him rotten with money.

Bob: Oh aye, that's the truth, he's as tight.

Bad egg

Bob: I had me table an' chairs out the back stowl last night.

Charlie: Och, not again.

Bob: The whole lot lifted. That's the second time the year.

Charlie: Any idea who it was?

Bob: Somebody who's after a tight hidin', that's who. I'd say it was yer man livin' beside the wife's brother.

Charlie: Thon boy steals everyhin' round him.

Bob: Ye'd need all nailed down when he's about.

Charlie: Sure he's never out of that court.

Bob: A bad egg surely. Wait till I get me hands on him.

Couldn' warm to him

Bob: See that buckin' eejit on that dur?

Charlie: I see him surely. Hair down to his backside.

Bob: Does he think he's Bob Geldof or what?

Bob: He's a jackass, that's what. He wouldn' let me in.

Charlie: He wouldn' let ye tax the car?

Bob: No, he says I have to do it on the line.

Charlie: Ye mean online?

Bob: Aye, have ye done it yerself?

Charlie: Not at all. Did ye not ask him how it's done?

Bob: He didn' want to help me one iota.

Charlie: Sure he's nohin' but a head-the-ball. Ye couldn' warm to him.

Would steal the eye out of yer head an' come back for the eyelashes

Bob: Yer man is just out of crowbar hotel.

Charlie: So the wife towl me. Ye'd want everyhin' under lock an' key, so.

Bob: Thornton was tellin' me he stowl eggs off him the day after gettin' out.

Charlie: Oh, he's a bad 'un.

Bob: If he dares put a foot on me street he'll know all about it.

Charlie: An' mine, I'll be waitin' for him with that stick.

Bob: A slap on the backside would sort him out.

Charlie: Is right.

Bob: Thon boy would steal the eye out of yer head an' come back for the eyelashes.

Hallion, *a mischief maker; a messer*

Bob: Yer man was at it again.

Charlie: Dippin'?

Bob: No, dortyin' that river.

Charlie: With the slurry, was it?

Bob: He knew rightly the tank was overflowin' an' did buck all about it.

Charlie: An' it seeped on down the field an' into the river?

Bob: That's exactly what happened. A pile of fish dead.

Charlie: The same boy would laugh about it.

Bob: An' it no laughin' matter.

Charlie: An' he'll do it again, ye mark me words.

Bob: He's a hallion.

Doin' the double, *to be drawing unemployment benefit and working on the quiet at the same time*

Bob: He's at it.

Charlie: Muldoon?

Bob: Oh, he's at it surely. He thinks we don't know.

Charlie: He doesn' do much to hide it, sure he doesn'.

Bob: Washin' windies an' pretendin' to be sick.

Charlie: What's supposed to be wrong with him?

Bob: He says he has that arthritis in the knees.

Charlie: An' yet he can get up an' down thon ladder.

Bob: He's doin' the double.

Thick ear

Bob: What about yer man hittin' the traffic warden with the frozen peas?

Charlie: Coulter? I heard that, wasn' that a downright disgrace.

Bob: Thon traffic warden should have lamped him.

Charlie: Sure ye can't hit anyone these days, not like before.

Bob: But he hit yer man across the forehead.

Charlie: I know, but ye can't hit members of the public back.

Bob: Ye should be able to, I'm tellin' ye.

Charlie: Sure is it any wonder the country's bucked.

Bob: If that had been me, Coulter would have got a thick ear.

Got away in the smoke

Bob: Why was the police outside yer wiman's house?

Charlie: Some man got into the house through the bathroom windie.

Bob: Did he steal anyhin'?

Charlie: He stowl a wireless an' one of them standard lamps.

Bob: In broad daylight?

Charlie: Aye, an' he didn' have a stitch on.

Bob: He was in the nip?

Charlie: He tore the trousers an' all off him gettin' in.

Bob: Did the police get him in the end up?

Charlie: Indeed they did not – he got away in the smoke.

Plastered

Bob: Did ye hear about McGurren comin' home on the bicycle?

Charlie: The wife said somehin', all right. Did he fall off it or what?

Bob: He went through Dane's wall, head over heels through the hedge.

Charlie: Did the brakes go or what was the matter?

Bob: It was more than the brakes that were gone.

Charlie: The whole head was gone, too?

Bob: Course. He was plastered. Sure he was drinkin' poitín in Thornton's shed for hours.

Charlie: Ever since he lost the licence he's gone to pot.

Bad article, *someone prone to getting into trouble; someone unsavoury*

Bob: One of me chickens is dead as a durnail.

Charlie: Ye're jokin' me.

Bob: I went down this mornin' an' it was lyin' there with the legs sprawled out.

Charlie: An oul blinkin' fox got it, I suppose.

Bob: I don't think so. I'd swear it was that boy next dur.

Charlie: Billy's cub? Yer man with the tattoo?

Bob: Aye, the one that looks like he was dragged through a hedge backways. His trouser legs were covered in feathers.

Charlie: Ye couldn' trust him as far as ye'd throw him.

Bob: Even me wife says he's a bad article.

That'll teach him

Bob: Thornton sliced the top of his finger cuttin' spuds.

Charlie: Ye don't have to tell me – I was there an' he was bleedin' like a pig.

Bob: Did ye tell him to stick it under the cowl tap?

Charlie: I did, but he got blood all over the delph.

Bob: He's always goin' on about how he can cook the tea.

Charlie: That man cannot cook, no more than the man on the moon.

Bob: Is it any wonder he cut himself then.

Charlie: That'll teach him for bletherin'.

He'll be all right if nohin' falls on him, *an expression indicating a lack of concern for someone else*

Bob: That blinkin' clown of a neighbour will get me boot yet.

Charlie: Is he still causin' a nuisance?

Bob: That wife of his sent him up here to give out about the slurry.

Charlie: Again? I wouldn' have even opened the dur to thon.

Bob: His wife's whingin' cause her washin' is on the line.

Charlie: An' what's wrong with that?

Bob: Och, says her pullover smells rotten.

Charlie: Her be damned.

Bob: Ye'd want to have seen the husband - roarin' he was.

Charlie: He'll be all right if nohin' falls on him.

Ye know the type of him

Bob: That big lanky eejit was hashin' again.

Charlie: He's the biggest pain in the backside.

Bob: Do ye know what he towl me this time?

Charlie: Nah, what now?

Bob: He says Mrs Kenwell can read tay leaves.

Charlie: Catch yerself on.

Bob: Oh aye, an' she towl him to buy one of them scratch cards.

Charlie: An' did he win somethin' on it?

Bob: He got three gold rings in a row. Fifty poun'.

Charlie: Ye're not serious. Can ye believe anyhin' he tells ye?

Bob: Take it with a pinch of salt - ye know the type of him.

Penny dropped

Bob: Are ye joinin' the protests about the milk prices the mara?

Charlie: Ye're damn right I am. That's our livelihoods, sure.

Bob: We're takin' a few of the tractors up to Stormount.

Charlie: I'd be up for that surely. Themuns need to listen.

Bob: There would be some row if we poured the milk away an' left them all with none.

Charlie: What would they put in their lattes then?

Bob: Well it wouldn' be long until the penny dropped.

He knows no more than the man on the moon

Bob: Thornton is mad to trace back his family tree.

Charlie: What is he at that for?

Bob: He's sure he's related to yer man O'Barack.

Charlie: Ye mean Barack Obama?

Bob: Aye, him - says he's about his sixteenth cousin removed.

Charlie: Och, pull the other one.

Bob: I was in the house last night an' he had oul maps an' all on the table.

Charlie: An' has he found much yet?

Bob: Just that the O'Baracks sold turf about Donegal.

Charlie: Would ye catch yerself on.

Bob: Thornton thinks he's on to somehin' here, that's the truth.

Charlie: He knows no more than the man on the moon.

Chapter Nine
Atein' an' Drinkin'

A hen for the pot

Bob: Such a day's work. I think me feet are about to fall off.

Charlie: I know what ye're sayin' - me bunions are flarin' away up.

Bob: I've some cream in the house for that.

Charlie: Oh, I'll take a wee bit if ye don't mind.

Bob: Not at all. Will we go in for a drop of tay an' a bite to eat?

Charlie: Aye, there's nohin' more we can do here till yer man comes to do the silage.

Bob: Right, I think the wife got a hen for the pot.

Would ye like a wee warmer? *Would you like a warm drop of tea in your cup?*

Bob: An' ye know it wasn' that long since he was thatchin' thon roof.

Charlie: I was just sayin' that to Father Curry, what, say, a month ago?

Bob: About that - just around then he was flat to the tin.

Charlie: Some crowd here the night, isn' t there?

Bob: Och, he was a civil crater, never hurt a one.

Charlie: Have ye enough tay there or do ye want more?

Bob: Sure I am still drinkin' the one they gave me when I came in.

Charlie: Here, would ye like a wee warmer, then so?

Life's too short

Bob: Japers, that was an awful pity about Mrs Traynor.

Charlie: Wasn' it? They say it was the fish pie she ate in thon place that kilt her.

Bob: So the wife was sayin'. Ye can ate nohin' these days.

Charlie: Two cubs an' a cat left behind, an' so soon after the husband.

Bob: She was to take that Pilates class next week an' all.

Charlie: Life's too short.

Chokin' with drooth, *very thirsty; dehydrated*

Bob: Whitewashin' thon wall is takin' up a bit of time.

Charlie: Isn't it? Ye just need to keep her goin' or ye'll never get it done.

Bob: I need to mix more watter an' lime an' then I'll be right.

Charlie: It'll look well when it's finished.

Bob: The wife's been moanin' at me all week to get it done.

Charlie: An' does she realise the work that goes into it?

Bob: Not at all. I'm tellin' ye, she hasn' a baldy.

Charlie: Are ye thirsty? I need a wee mineral or somehin'.

Bob: I am chokin' with drooth. Have ye any brown lemonade in the house?

Don't agree with me

Bob: Well, did ye get them stones gathered up?

Charlie: I did not, I wasn' able to stoop once.

Bob: Och now, why was that?

Charlie: I was up pukin' in a basin the whole night.

Bob: Was it somehin' ye ate?

Charlie: I had a burger at the show yisterday an' it had onions on it.

Bob: Them things would go through me, so they would.

Charlie: I thought I'd take a wee chance an' try one, but they don't agree with me at all so they don't.

Go spare

Bob: Here, have ye ever seen one of these things?

Charlie: Is that one of them blenders?

Bob: Aye - ye throw fruit an' veg an' all into it.

Charlie: An' ye drink that muck?

Bob: Oh aye, it's good if ye've cramp.

Charlie: The wife says I don't eat enough fruit.

Bob: Well, I try an' have a melon in the evenins.

Charlie: Hard to bate a sausage bap though.

Bob: Don't say another word.

Charlie: Wee bit of brown sauce.

Bob: If I ate one of them now the wife would go spare.

Foosies, *small, sweet biscuits*

Bob: I've to go see me dentist – I lost a tooth last night.

Charlie: How did ye manage that? Atein' somehin' hard, I suppose.

Bob: They were handin' out chocolate digestives at the lassie's birthday party.

Charlie: The wife damaged her own dentures on a Wagon Wheel.

Bob: It's no joke, ye know.

Charlie: I know. Ye'd want to see the bake on her; it's like she swallowed a wasp.

Bob: Did she go to the dentist herself then?

Charlie: Didn' bother, she's the dentures steepin' in the sink.

Bob: She'll know for again to cut down on the foosies, like meself.

Head-the-ball, *someone who is as daft as a brush*

Bob: Have ye ever had Father Curry about the house?

Charlie: Aye, he was in there the other night for a drop of tay.

Bob: He was in ours earlier an' he must have stayed three hours.

Charlie: What did ye talk about for three hours?

Bob: Everyhin' an' anyhin'. An' he ate us out of house an' home.

Charlie: He'd be a quare ater.

Bob: Is right. He ate the last of me favourite biscuits, as well.

Charlie: An' was he sayin' much?

Bob: He was sayin' he's wile into that yoga thing.

Charlie: Throwin' the legs about?

Bob: Aye, an' lyin' on yer back with the whole lot in the air.

Charlie: He's a head-the-ball.

Packed to the gills, *full*

Bob: No, I don't believe ye.

Charlie: I am tellin' ye, I did.

Bob: Ye cooked for yerself an' the wife?

Charlie: I had no choice ever since she twisted the ankle.

Bob: An' what did ye make?

Charlie: I made spuds an' butter.

Bob: Any vegetables?

Charlie: A few peas, couple of carrots.

Bob: An' did she enjoy the feed?

Charlie: She did, an' she said she was packed to the gills.

Not firin' on all cylinders

Bob: Have ye ever had lamb kebabs?

Charlie: I wouldn' be a big lamb ater.

Bob: That cub of mine brought some home to try last night.

Charlie: What's a kebab when it's at home?

Bob: It's an oul thing on a stick.

Charlie: What would ye ate that muck for?

Bob: It wasn't too bad at all, apart from the peppers.

Charlie: That cub of yers musn' be well, atein' thon.

Bob: He wouldn' be firin' on all cylinders.

Full as a frog

Bob: Ye ever try them Kerr's Pinks?

Charlie: Oh aye, there'd be plenty of atein' in thon.

Bob: I've some growin' over yonder if ye want to take a handful.

Charlie: I'll take some surely; the wife'll be thankful of them this evenin'.

Bob: I had a fierce feed of spuds when I came home from the mart.

Charlie: I'd say that would have kept ye goin' till ye got into yer bed.

Bob: Och, it did surely. I was full as a frog.

Wet the tay, *to pour the water on to the teabags or tea leaves*

Bob: Will ye soon be home or what?

Charlie: I'm lookin' the town for a new pair of wellingtons.

Bob: What kind are ye after?

Charlie: The oul-fashioned rubber ones.

Bob: Try the Dunlops, they've the special sole.

Charlie: That's the ones I'm after surely.

Bob: How long will ye be? I'll throw the kettle on, sure.

Charlie: Aye, wet the tay, an' I'll be back soon enough.

Full as a tick

Bob: The lassie brought us out for a feed last night.

Charlie: Where'd ye all go?

Bob: We went to one of them Indian places.

Charlie: But sure would that stuff not burn the mouth off ye?

Bob: It's not bad, ye know, but they fairly spoon the food onto the plate.

Charlie: A pile of stuff, I suppose. Did ye ate much?

Bob: I never stopped, I had to open the belt of me trousers to let the belly out.

Charlie: Ye were full as a tick, then so.

Fadge, *homemade potato bread*

Bob: Give me a fried egg, a bit of bacon an' a wee spoon of beans.

Charlie: Aye, I'll have the same as himself, an' two slices of toast.

Bob: Here, Charlie, do ye want a pot of tay or coffee?

Charlie: I'll have a cup of coffee, for a wee change.

Bob: It's not a bad wee spot, this.

Charlie: They do a right trade every mornin'.

Bob: Och, I forgot to ask the wee lassie for a bit of fadge.

142

A feed that would have kilt a horse

Bob: Japers, the wife put on some stuff for Christmas.

Charlie: I know all about it, I had to open me belt in me own house.

Bob: She had turkey an' spuds an' carrots an' ye name it on that plate.

Charlie: Did ye try a wee Yorkshire puddin' like I towl ye to?

Bob: I did an' I threw a wee jug of gravy all over the whole lot.

Charlie: That would have filled a hole. Ye're well looked after, then so.

Bob: I am, she made a feed that would have kilt a horse.

Delph, *glazed earthenware crockery, often blue and white*

Bob: What time is this over? I've to fodder the cattle before the night's out.

Charlie: Och, the wife says it'll be no longer than an hour.

Bob: I don't know why I have to do a health an' safety course. Sure there was no such thing when I was a cub.

Charlie: That's right, ye just fell over an' got up again.

Bob: I mind sprainin' the ankle an' doin' a day's work afterwards.

Charlie: Here, whisht a minute, they're givin' out tay first.

Bob: There's yer wiman Mrs Saunderson comin' with a tray of stuff.

Charlie: Japers, she's carryin' some amount of fancy delph.

What use is that to me?

Bob: The lassie brought me into one of them tay shops in the town.

Charlie: Ye would have spent a poun' or two in there.

Bob: I was that hungry, I thought I was goin' to pass out.

Charlie: What did ye get to ate?

Bob: They give me a samwidge, well, it wouldn' have filt a hole in me tooth.

Charlie: Not like the food ye would have got long ago.

Bob: It was about the size of a postage stamp an' ye'd want to see the thing they gave us to drink.

Charlie: Some oul fancy thing, I suppose.

Bob: It was one of them skinny lattes if ye ever heard of them. The lassie wanted thon thing. I said, at that price, it would want to be a fat latte.

Charlie: Now, a drop of normal tay is hard to bate.

Bob: Ye're right, Charlie. A latte. What use is that to me?

Wouldn' have filled a hole in yer tooth, *food that is insubstantial; of meagre proportions*

Bob: The cub brought me to an oul thing at that Hillsborough Castle.

Charlie: Get away, I hope ye were lookin' well for herself.

Bob: I combed the hair an' that was about it.

Charlie: That would be a quare place to look 'round.

Bob: There's a fierce bit of ground to it.

Charlie: An' did they feed ye or what?

Bob: There were cocktail sausages on a stick.

Charlie: Any samwidges?

Bob: Aye, but they wouldn' have filled a hole in yer tooth.

There's good atein' in that, *a substantial item or meal*

Bob: Here, what else do ye want with yer tay?

Charlie: Och, I'll take a bit of that Victoria sponge.

Bob: Nice place this. Annette hasn' it open too long.

Charlie: Not bad at all, an' ye get some stuff for

yer money.

Bob: Well, look at the size of thon cake she's give ye. There's good atein in that.

Charlie: That'll do me all day, that.

Rabbit food

Bob: The wife says I am gettin' as round as a barrel.

Charlie: Ye're gettin' a bit of a belly on ye all right.

Bob: Ye're one to talk - ye've been lopsided this ten years.

Charlie: That's to do with the pain in me back, not me weight.

Bob: Well anyway, she has me atein' them oul pumpkin seeds.

Charlie: Get-away-a-that, she has not.

Bob: An' a pile of nuts like I'm a blinkin' squirrel.

Charlie: That wife of mine put lettuce on the plate yisterday.

Bob: Japers, Charlie. There's nohin' I hate more than that oul rabbit food.

I'm good but I'm not that good

Bob: Here, I made the dinner on Sunday, so I did.

Charlie: Did you do the spuds an' vegetables an' all?

Bob: I did surely.

Charlie: An' the gravy?

Bob: Her indoors said it was the best she'd ever had. She had to open her belt.

Charlie: Did ye make a wee crumble or somehin' for afters?

Bob: Not at all – I'm good but I'm not that good.

Never cast a clout till May be out, *keep your winter clothes until summer has properly arrived*

Bob: Have ye any margarine for these baps?

Charlie: What's wrong with butter?

Bob: They say it sends the cholesterol mad.

Charlie: Yer arse. What time is the barbecue?

Bob: After *Emmerdale Farm*.

Charlie: The weather isn't too bad, I'll take the raincoat off, then so.

Bob: Do not. Never cast a clout till May be out.

Chapter Ten
The Weather

It'll depend on the weather

Bob: Such a clatty day.

Charlie: We'll not get that last field done now.

Bob: Not at all, not until it eases a bit.

Charlie: Does it do anyhin' but teem out of the heavens?

Bob: It's not even waitin' to rain.

Charlie: Ye need to get yerself a good warm coat.

Bob: I had one with a couple of layers but didn' the dog rip it to bits.

Charlie: We'll have to look about finishin' thon job the mara, then so.

Charlie: Here, it'll depend on the weather.

Foundered, *frozen; chilled to the bone*

Bob: There was a tight frost last night, boy.

Charlie: I know there was - I've been out tryin' to salt the path.

Bob: Ye'd want to go easy or ye'll fall flat on yer face.

Charlie: I nearly did, there's no grips on these boots of mine.

Bob: Me drinkin' trough is all froze over, too.

Charlie: Would ye credit it? Frank Mitchell didn' give that.

Bob: Indeed, he did not. I can't get warmed up at all.

Charlie: I'm foundered.

Dead hate, *intolerable heat*

Bob: I need a drink of watter.

Charlie: Get me a drop, too, will ye?

Bob: I'm chokin' so I am.

Charlie: Was it this hot when we were cuttin' thon tree?

Bob: Not at all, it just came on there all of a sudden.

Charlie: It's hard to stick that, I may take me pullover off.

Bob: I've one of them short-sleeved shirts on under this.

Charlie: Ye'd need it a day like thon.

Bob: It would roast ye.

Charlie: There's an awful dead hate.

The roads are like a bottle, *the roads are so icy that they are like glass*

Bob: I was out pickin' up the pension this mornin'.

Charlie: Many on the road?

Bob: Not many at all, it was right quiet the whole way in.

Charlie: That's the bad weather ye see, people stayin' indurs.

Bob: Ye'd be as well inside, that's the truth.

Charlie: I've to run to the chemist for the wife. How bad is it?

Bob: I was slippin' an' slidin' down that road of mine.

Charlie: The council hasn' salted it again, I suppose.

Bob: The roads are like a bottle.

Teemin', *pouring (rain)*

Bob: Are ye goin' to this thing at the church hall?

Charlie: Is that the thing Father Curry is doin'?

Bob: Aye, the wife's makin' buns an' tay an' all for it.

Charlie: Curry asked me to bring a lock of fowl.

Bob: I'll head after I scrape the last of this wallpaper off the bedroom.

Charlie: Will ye run me down to it?

Bob: I will surely, but we'll not be long. It gives rain.

Charlie: It'll be teemin' all evenin' surely.

It might ease

Bob: Do ye hear the rattles of thon?

Charlie: I do, an' there's a bit of lightnin' too.

Bob: There's another flash.

Charlie: The wife hates the thunder.

Bob: Mine's the same – everyhin' has to be pulled out of the wall.

Charlie: Mine lies in the bed with the cover over her head.

Bob: There'd be people like that surely.

Charlie: Here, it would want to soon settle for I've the goats to feed.

Bob: It might ease soon enough.

There's great dryin' out, *there's great weather for drying clothes on the line outside*

Bob: There's a quare change in the weather.

Charlie: Isn't there a change surely?

Bob: An' it's good to see it.

Charlie: It fairly gives ye a wee lift.

Bob: Sure it was bucketin' earlier.

Charlie: I know all about it - I wet the leg of me trousers in a puddle.

Bob: As long as the sun stays for a bit longer till I get them stones lifted.

Bob: Well, that's not a bad day now.

Charlie: There's great dryin' out.

Bucketin' out of the heavens

Bob: We're late again but are we ever anyhin' else?

Charlie: Sure we had to bring the cattle in.

Bob: Herself said if I missed the start of this christenin' she'd give me what for.

Charlie: Sure mine said she'd give me dinner to the dog.

Bob: I didn' have time to put on me good shoes either.

Charlie: Nobody will see ye. Ye'd only ruin them anyway in thon.

Bob: Ye're right - they'd be soakin'.

Charlie: Course they would. It's bucketin' out of the heavens.

Clatty oul day, *a grey, miserable day*

Bob: The wife's at me to lose a few poun'.

Charlie: Are ye gettin' a belly on ye?

Bob: There might be a wee bit hangin' over all right.

Charlie: Too much atein' - she's too good to ye.

Bob: She's at me to walk the roads in the evenin'.

Charlie: That's right popular these days. They're all at it.

Bob: I need to get meself a pair of them short trousers.

Charlie: Are ye goin' walkin' the day?

Bob: How would ye walk in thon?

Charlie: Aye, that's a clatty oul day.

At least it's dry

Bob: I might get a bit of paintin' done the day.

Charlie: Are ye goin' to do the front of the house like ye said?

Bob: Well, herself seems to have her mind made up.

Charlie: An' ye're goin' for crame?

Bob: It's more of a mustardy colour, to tell ye the truth.

Charlie: Ye should get plenty done the day.

Bob: I've the overalls on - just need a bit of pace to do it.

Charlie: At least it's dry.

Have ye ever seen rain like it?

Bob: Ye'd want to put them wipers on another bit.

Charlie: They're goin' as fast as they can.

Bob: Sure ye can barely see out the windie.

Charlie: They'll not go up any further.

Bob: That's wile.

Charlie: I may pull in till she passes.

Bob: Ye can stop at the shop, I've a few wee messages to get.

Charlie: I've to bring home firelighters.

Bob: An' I think we're out of toilet roll.

Charlie: Japers, have ye ever seen rain like it?

Quare ball of weather, *a period of exceedingly warm weather*

Bob: That Thornton boy never shuts his bake. He talks a mile a minute.

Charlie: It's all them tablets he's on, ye see, puttin' him off his head all together.

Bob: If he'd settle, I'd help him toss the bottom meadow.

Charlie: Ye should wait till it's a bit cooler, should ye not?

Bob: Och, it'll not take too long.

Charlie: But the hate will make it harder to get things done.

Bob: Well, will he mind if we were to do it the mara instead?

Charlie: Not at all. Sure there's a quare ball of weather.

Cowl, *cold*

Bob: Would ye believe I've two pairs of socks on me the day?

Charlie: I would believe ye - the wind would go through ye.

Bob: Thon Barra Best fella gave it bad all week.

Charlie: Aye well, he got it right for once. There was no hate last night. I had to put a jar in the bed.

Bob: The wife put two of them in ours.

Charlie: Don't they warm up the bed - ye just have to mind not to burn the toes of yerself.

Bob: An' it's suppose to be the middle of the summer.

Charlie: Cowl from mornin' to night? That's no summer.

There's a right stretch in the evenin'

Bob: The cub's movin' out so I've to give him a hand to flit.

Charlie: Have ye enough boxes in the house?

Bob: Oh aye, sure he doesn' have much to his name.

Charlie: Are ye throwin' all in the trailer?

Bob: I am - two trips there an' back should be enough.

Charlie: Ye'll get that done the day, then so.

Bob: Aye, that's a brave day, sure.

Charlie: There's a right stretch in the evenin'.

Does it know what it's doin' at all?

Bob: I had the big coat on me this mornin' an' I just had to take it off.

Charlie: Did ye see the size of them hailstones?

Bob: I did, they were bouncin' off the windies.

Charlie: An' the howl of the wind - I thought I was goin' to lose the wife.

Bob: I wouldn' be lucky enough to lose mine.

Charlie: Don't let her hear ye say that or ye'll know all about it.

Bob: I just felt a big drop of rain on me nose. It's at it again.

Charlie: Does it know what it's doin' at all?

It's been tryin' to snow all day

Bob: I've been tryin' to fix the boiler for the last lock of hours.

Charlie: What's wrong with it? Lakin' is it?

Bob: No, there's not a kick out of it.

Charlie: So it's not hatin' up the house?

Bob: It'll do nohin' for me.

Charlie: Are ye sure ye're not just out of oil?

Bob: We got three drums a week an' a half ago.

Charlie: Well, ye need the hate. It's been tryin' to snow all day.

It'll improve when the childers back to school

Bob: It was quern dull this mornin' when I was feedin' them hens.

Charlie: It's been a bad summer altogether.

Bob: Them granchilder of mine were indurs every day of the week.

Charlie: Sure, what good is that to them?

Bob: I know. They were flat out playin' them Play Station things on the television.

Charlie: They'll get square eyes from thon.

Bob: I said that to them, but they couldn' have gone outside in the cowl.

Charlie: Och, ye're right. They'd only get a chill.

Bob: It'll improve when the childers back to school.

Fierce day for the silage, *a great day for cutting silage*

Bob: Japers, ye've the shirt an' all off ye.

Charlie: I've been workin' from early mornin'.

Bob: What has ye up all mornin'?

Charlie: I've been lyin' on me back under thon tractor.

Bob: An' is she fixed yet after all that clannin' about?

Charlie: Och, I'll say she'll be right for that job of ours.

Bob: Well, it's a good day to get all done.

Charlie: Fierce day for the silage surely.

Nip in the air

Bob: Do ye want red sauce on yer burger?

Charlie: Aye, give us a wee dab of it. Not too much.

Bob: That new barbecue is some job.

Charlie: It's great to be able to sit outside an' ate.

Bob: Ye'd get bored in the house, wouldn' ye but.

Charlie: Ah, ye would surely. Ye'd go spare.

Bob: An' ye could sit out in thon no bother.

Charlie: Aye, still, there's a wee nip in the air.

Is it ever goin' to pick up at all? *Will the weather ever improve?*

Bob: Ye know what me an' the wife worked out there?

Charlie: What?

Bob: It's about three weeks since there was a bit of sun.

Charlie: It is not.

Bob: Aye, I'll tell ye when we last had some, too. Gaby's funeral.

Charlie: I think ye're right, ye know.

Bob: Mind, we were carryin' the coffin an' I could barely see where I was goin'.

Charlie: Is right. Ye nearly tripped over Mrs Swift's husband's grave.

Bob: I was squintin' away, do ye mind?

Charlie: I do.

Bob: Is it ever goin' to pick up at all?

Sun is splittin' the stones, *a very hot day*

Bob: Do ye know what I need for them feet of mine?

Charlie: I don't think I want to know.

Bob: Sandpaper. I've bunions the size of potatoes, that's the truth.

Charlie: Is it sore when ye walk?

Bob: It is, an' it's worser with the warm weather.

Charlie: I'd say so.

Bob: I'm doin' an awful bit of limpin' about.

Charlie: Get yerself a pair of them sandals for yer feet.

Bob: They'd fairly help when the sun is splittin' the stones.

Burnt to a crisp

Bob: I heard about the wife – how is she now?

Charlie: Not great – she's as red as a tomata, to be honest.

Bob: That Benidorm place, was it?

Charlie: Aye, she went over with that sister of hers.

Bob: An' what happened?

Charlie: She forgot the glasses an' thought the cream for her ankles was suncream.

Bob: Japers, an' threw it all on?

Charlie: Every nook an' cranny. She came back yisterday, burnt to a crisp.

Ye can't see the hand in front of yer face

Bob: I've that oak tree to take out an' replant.

Charlie: Ye picked a bad day to do it.

Bob: The cub said he'd help me - it's his tree.

Charlie: Did he grow it himself?

Bob: He did, from an acorn.

Charlie: An' now ye're movin' it.

Bob: I'd move it if I could see the blinkin' thing.

Charlie: Ye can't see the hand in front of yer face that day.

Skiff of rain, *a light shower*

Bob: The wife's standin' in thon town, collectin'.

Charlie: Who she doin' that for?

Bob: One of them charities. I can't mind what ye call them now.

Charlie: An' does she have a long stand or what?

Bob: Och, she could be out there for a lock of hours anyway.

Charlie: She's a good 'un to keep that goin'.

Bob: That friend of hers with the clubfoot has her out.

Charlie: The weather's not too bad so far anyway.

Bob: Well, there's to be a skiff of rain later but she's her umbrella with her.

Between the showers

Bob: I've to pick up a new suite of furniture.

Charlie: From the town or what?

Bob: No, that Conway boy down the road is sellin' one.

Charlie: New or second hand? Much he lookin'?

Bob: Second hand. He's after eighty poun' an' a stone of spuds.

Charlie: Will ye get it up to the house on yer own?

Bob: I've the tractor an' trailer ready to go.

Charlie: Have ye anyhin' to throw over it?

Bob: There's a couple of fertiliser bags in the back.

Charlie: Not so bad.

Bob: I'll get her moved between the showers.

Hop up well, *wrap up well*

Bob: I was out last night for a bucket of sticks an' the animals were roarin'.

Charlie: Were they all right?

Bob: I couldn' get them settled at all.

Charlie: Was it the cowl night? There was a bitter frost.

Bob: I don't know, but I was standin' in thon shed for an hour an' a half.

Charlie: An' ye with yer stomach cramps an' all.

Bob: Och, but sure didn' I hop up well.

There's a wind out there that would clane corn

Bob: Did ye lose yer wheelie bin this mornin'?

Charlie: I lost more than me wheelie bin – the washin' on the line went too.

Bob: Me bin ended up in yer man's front garden. Such a wind.

Charlie: I can't find half the washin' an' the wife will go off her head.

Bob: Have ye lost much?

Charlie: A few of me socks, an' the wife's bloomers.

Bob: Sure ye couldn' keep anyhin' down in thon.

Charlie: Is right. There's a wind out there that would clane corn.

Changeable

Bob: That dog of yers is gettin' a quare size.

Charlie: Isn't he? He can barely walk, that's the truth.

Bob: What are ye feedin' him? Big dinners or what?

Charlie: That's the wife – she throws everyhin' at him.

Bob: Like what?

Charlie: Bits a turkey breast – she says he likes turkey. He's better fed than meself.

Bob: Ye'd want to take him out now for a big long walk.

Charlie: Would ye believe I was about to, but it looks like it's goin' to pour again.

Bob: Aye, them clouds are closin' in.

Charlie: It's very changeable.

It wouldn' wet yer cap

Bob: I am in for the rest of the day an' I'll not be movin' off this chair.

Charlie: But, sure are ye not givin' me a hand to varnish the dur?

Bob: I was up this mornin' before the rooster started crowin'.

Charlie: C'mon, it'll not take ye two minutes.

Bob: Ye'd look well varnishin' a dur an' it spittin'.

Charlie: There's no rain - that's all in yer head.

Bob: Do ye think I was born yisterday? Look outside.

Charlie: It wouldn' wet yer cap.

Chapter Eleven
Not in My Day

Happy as a pig in muck

Bob: Do ye remember oul man McVitty about the place?

Charlie: I don't. Was that back in yer father's time?

Bob: It would have been. He was a quare character an' some worker. He would have worked till he nearly dropped, an' didn' expect a shillin'.

Charlie: Not like now. Sure them kind of boys are a dyin' breed.

Bob: Don't I know it. All he wanted was a gravy dinner.

Charlie: I don't believe ye.

Bob: A gravy dinner an' he was as happy as a pig in muck.

He'd fall out with his own shadow

Bob: That Rory Mackerel is a quare good golfer, isn't he?

Charlie: Do ye not mean McIlroy?

Bob: Maybe, I do. He's fairly makin' the money.

Charlie: An' all for hittin' a wee ball with a stick.

Bob: Did ye see him throw the club into the watter?

Charlie: I did, there's a man wouldn' be long losin' the temper.

Bob: I'd say he'd fall out with his own shadow.

Fibbin'

Bob: Ye ever see these jeans the young ones are wearin' now with the holes in them?

Charlie: Such a lookin' sight.

Bob: What's the sense in them?

Charlie: They wouldn' be much good to ye, shovellin' silage on a frosty mornin.

Bob: An' not chape either.

Charlie: Not at all, an' no knees in them.

Bob: The cub says his cost twenty-five poun'.

Charlie: I doubt he's fibbin'. Sixty poun' wouldn' have a look in.

There's always somethin'

Bob: Have ye got an Apple?

Charlie: Like a Granny Smith or what?

Bob: Not at all, ye clart. One of them 'puter things.

Charlie: How in blue blazes do ye know what one of them is?

Bob: The cuttie has her face glued to one all that time. Now she has to wear glasses.

Charlie: Is that so?

Bob: Sure it's no time since she had to wear the eye patch because of all the textin'.

Charlie: Sure, isn't there always somehin'.

It'll not happen twice

Bob: I was buyin' slug pellets down in yer man's shop this mornin'.

Charlie: Och no, have ye problems with them blinkin' slugs?

Bob: Aye, they're atein' me tomata plants the whole time.

Charlie: A blinkin' nuisance, that's what they are.

Bob: An' here, didn' the cub behind the counter charge me for the plastic bag.

Charlie: That's right, sure ye have to pay 5p for them now.

Bob: I couldn' believe it, for a buckin' bag.

Charlie: Ye'd be as well carryin' a bag with ye the whole time.

Bob: I give him the 5p, but I tell ye, it'll not happen twice.

Clampit, *an idiot*

Bob: It must be election time again.

Charlie: Aye, they're back knockin' the durs again.

Bob: Well, mark me words, they'll not be gettin' in here.

Charlie: Sure that's the only time ye see them – votin' time. There's not one of them worth a damn, not like the ones ye had years ago.

Bob: Give them me vote? I'd give them a boot in the arse quicker.

Charlie: We had yer man at the dur last night.

Bob: Who was that?

Charlie: Mind the one that claimed the expenses for the pencil.

Bob: Och aye, that clampit.

Scandal

Bob: The childer are always crowin' about walkin' to the bus shilter.

Charlie: They'd have done some whingin' back in our day.

Bob: I mind walkin' to school in me bare feet, that's the truth.

Charlie: There wasn' one shoe about the house.

Bob: Sure there wasn' much money to spend on shoes or laces.

Charlie: We would have walked miles every day.

Bob: An' ye maybe wouldn' have had anyhin' to ate all day.

Charlie: A bit of bread would have been about the height of it.

Bob: Not like now – these ones don't know they're livin'.

Charlie: It's a real scandal, so it is.

Malarkey

Bob: These wimen expect all sorts nowadays, don't they, but?

Charlie: They want wined an' dined, so they do.

Bob: I mind when a few fluers would have done rightly.

Charlie: Ye'd have got the curt handy enough, so.

Bob: Now they're lookin' a pile of things.

Charlie: That's right, like that oul stuff ye spray under yer arms.

Bob: An' shoes ye can barely walk a straight line in.

Charlie: That's the shoes with the raised heels?

Bob: Ye wouldn' be long breakin' yer neck in them.

Charlie: See these shoes of mine? Fierce strong leather, not even scuffed.

Bob: An' sturdy too, I'd say, not like that high-heeled malarkey.

Isn't it tellin' him, *isn't he the lucky one*

Bob: What about that clown in the council?

Charlie: Yer man that sweats all the time?

Bob: Aye. It says in that paper he's gettin' a big pay-off.

Charlie: Sure he's only through the dur.

Bob: They last no time nowadays before they get off on the sick, ye see.

Charlie: Yer man hasn' done one thing for any of us.

Bob: Payin' our rates so he can go on another holiday.

Charlie: Isn't it tellin' him.

I'd knock him down with me cap

Bob: Yer man Paddy Barnes is a hardy boy.

Charlie: That's the boxer cub? Not at all. Ye could put him in yer pocket he's that small.

Bob: Here, he must be atein' his spuds, ye should see the beef on him.

Charlie: He's not like that Muhammad Ally, do ye mind him? He was some fella. This Barnes boy is as thin as a rake, I could take him on surely.

Bob: Och, ye could not - don't be so daft.

Charlie: I'd knock him down with me cap.

Flummoxed

Bob: See the council wants to charge ye for feedin' the ducks now.

Charlie: What do ye mean, charge ye?

Bob: They want to charge ye 20p to feed them down by the watter.

Charlie: What's wrong with throwin' a bit of bread at them?

Bob: Ye're not suppose to do that, they say. A bit of bird seed instead.

Charlie: 20p a time? Have ye ever heard anyhin' like it in all yer life?

Bob: I am flummoxed, that's the truth.

Wouldn' it sicken ye

Bob: Them politicians get some expenses, don't they?

Charlie: Did ye hear about yer man claimin' for a pullover for his dog?

Bob: A pullover for the dog? I don't believe ye.

Charlie: I'm tellin' ye, it had a Christmas tree on it an' flashin' lights.

Bob: I've heard it all now. That's a blinkin' disgrace.

Charlie: He claimed for a scarf for the dog, too.

Bob: Och, don't tell me that.

Charlie: Wouldn' it sicken ye.

Themuns

Bob: They do some hashin' in that Stormount every day.

Charlie: Don't they just. They're never done yappin' at each other.

Bob: Sortin' things out, that's what they should be at.

Charlie: An' yer man's always givin' out about the other boy.

Bob: That's right, an' herself throws the wee doll some looks.

Charlie: They'd want their heads knocked together, that's the truth.

Bob: Themuns. Will they ever learn at all?

Knee high to a grasshopper

Bob: Look at the size of thon house.

Charlie: Japers, it must be about three storeys, that's the truth.

Bob: Is there any need for all them windies?

Charlie: An' what would ye want two chimneys for?

Bob: Ye wouldn' be lightin' the fire twice, would ye?

Charlie: I suppose if ye were cowl enough ye might.

Bob: They done away with some hedges for thon place.

Charlie: Sure they have it all destroyed now.

Bob: When I was knee high to a grasshopper this was all green fields.

Choppin' an' changin'

Bob: I was tryin' to send a letter to the brother in Wales. Such a handlin'.

Charlie: Could ye not mind his address or what?

Bob: Not at all, it was the blinkin' stamp.

Charlie: They're some price now, so they are.

Bob: It wasn' even that, it kept fallin' off the envelope.

Charlie: Did ye not lick the buckin' thing?

Bob: I must have licked it for ten minutes flat, an' nohin'.

Charlie: Why would that be, I wonder?

Bob: The lassie behind the counter said they have a sticky back now.

Charlie: Och right, ye have to peel them, not lick them.

Bob: Sure they're always choppin' an' changin' things these days.

No pace

Bob: Would yer house be as mad as our house with the granchilder?

Charlie: I'd say so - sure they're into everyhin'.

Bob: Back in my day, childer were seen but not heard.

Charlie: Isn't that how it should be, instead of all this clannin' about?

Bob: An' see all this huggin', such a bit of carryin' on.

Charlie: They do that for the pocket money, ye see.

Bob: When I was thon age I would have got a thrupenny bit.

Charlie: More than meself - I'd have got an orange if I was lucky.

Bob: Here, all I want now is a bit of pace after a hard day's work.

Yarn

Bob: It's all about these bloomin' texes these days.

Charlie: Nobody wants to even look at one another now.

Bob: Too much bother to even lift their heads, that's the truth.

Charlie: That's the childer for ye, they haven' a blinkin' notion.

Bob: Ye need to look a man straight in the eye.

Charlie: That's the way to do it, not them oul phones.

Bob: An' talk – there's nohin' wrong with a bit of hashin'.

Charlie: Or comin' into the kitchen for tay an' a yarn.

Parful

Bob: The lights went out in the house last night.

Charlie: Did ye find yer way about?

Bob: I got up to go to the toilet an' hit me toe off the skirtin' board.

Charlie: The bulbs these days last no time, ye know, sure they don't?

Bob: Them screw-in things? Not at all, no blinkin' good.

Charlie: Ye'd fairly miss the oil lamps, wouldn' ye?

Bob: Japers, there was some light off them when they were on.

Charlie: They would have lit up the whole house.

Bob: A parful job surely.

As scarce as hen's teeth

Bob: They don't make buckets like they used to.

Charlie: The ones nowadays are not worth a fiddlers.

Bob: An' they carry nohin' either, that's the truth.

Charlie: I know all about it, ye'd want to hear what happened me yisterday.

Bob: What happened ye?

Charlie: I was carryin' feed to the calves an' the arse fell out of the bucket.

Bob: See, didn' I say that? They're no good at all.

Charlie: The birds had the whole lot ate by the time I went to clane it up.

Bob: A good bucket is as scarce as hen's teeth.

Sure, why would ye not?

Bob: The granchild was askin' me what the whole thing was about.

Charlie: What's what about?

Bob: What life is about.

Charlie: That's some spake for a child. What age is this cub?

Bob: He's about seven. He asked me to sum it up in one word.

Charlie: An' what did ye tell him?

Bob: I said to him, 'Son, I do have one word to sum it all up–'

Charlie: Aye?

Bob: 'An' that word is … love.'

Charlie: Here, ye're a big softie at heart.

Bob: I told him if he found a wee wiman as good as his grandma, he'd be doin' all right.

Charlie: An' right ye are.

Bob: Love. Sure, why would ye not?

Acknowledgements

You are only as good as those around you and I am very fortunate to be surrounded by so many talented and inspiring people. Without the unwavering support, wisdom and extraordinary kindness of each of them, this book would have been utterly impossible.

I am enormously grateful to Blackstaff Press for taking a chance on me and giving me the opportunity to write my first book. Thank you in particular to Patsy Horton, Jim Meredith and Helen Wright, my inarguably brilliant editor, for the guidance and enthusiasm throughout. Thank you also to my hugely talented illustrator Karen Harbinson for bringing Bob and Charlie to life.

Thanks to Sarah Saunderson, my editor at *The Impartial Reporter*, for not just allowing me the freedom to write a book but for assisting me at every stage of the process, and for coming up with the suitably hilarious title. She has been a fan of Bob and Charlie from the beginning so I am delighted to have reached this stage thanks to her assistance. I smile when I think of our many conversations about Bob and Charlie that were spent laughing out loud.

He was responsible for kick-starting my career at *The Impartial Reporter* all those years ago, so it was wonderful to have had the help of my mentor Denzil McDaniel during this project. He has taught me many things, not least the importance of perseverance and patience, both in life and work. There was no better person to launch my book than the man who made all of this possible.

Thanks to Brigid Jones who gave up so much of her time

to assist in discussions, reading, editing and thinking. She has been a constant, invaluable tower of strength from the very beginning of this project, and right up to the end. This book simply would not have happened without her.

Thanks to Julie Kenwell and Meadhbh Monahan, and all my colleagues at *The Impartial Reporter* for their help, including John McVitty, Gareth Cauldwell, Mark Conway, Lily Dane, Corinna Power, Avril Anderson, Jonathan Rainey, Robert Forde, June Clarke and Brian Donaldson, to whom I am particularly grateful to for his many superb comments and suggestions.

Thanks to Julian Thornton, Sean Paul Curry and Jonathan Bailey, three of the funniest men around, for the hours and hours of hilarity during the planning and writing process, and for helping me mould the characters of Bob and Charlie and others. Their help made it all so much easier.

Thanks to Noel Edwards, Laura Patterson, Jim Ledwith, Joe Mahon, Johnny McKeegan, Pat Monaghan and Noel Johnston for reminding me of some terrific words and phrases.

I am very thankful for the encouraging words of wisdom from so many, including my grandma; my sister Annette; the Dean of Clogher, the Very Reverend Kenneth Hall; Father Brian D'Arcy; Trevor Birney; Niall McCracken; Marion Maxwell; Paul Breen; Jason Johnson; Rebecca Black; Joanne Wilson; Donna Whyte; Tim McGarry; Hugo Duncan; Stuart Coulter; and Eamonn Holmes.

Special, heartfelt thanks to John Bennett and to the following people and their families, for all they have done to help, not just during this project: Gary and Joanne Black; Colin and Joan Robinson.

And a massive thank you to anyone who has ever read any of my articles, including my 'Fermanagh Spake' column, in *The Impartial Reporter*. Your support, loyalty and kindness is not lost on me, and I appreciate it as much today as I did when I started writing when I was sixteen.

Finally, because I don't say it enough, a huge thank you to my parents who have always supported me in everything I have done and are just as excited about my first book as I am.